Philosophy

Herbert Spencer

The Intellectual Legacy

Edited by
Greta Jones and
Robert A Peel

The Galton Institute

Herbert Spencer
The Intellectual Legacy

Proceedings of a Conference organised by the Galton
Institute, London, 2003

Edited by

Greta Jones and Robert Peel

PUBLISHED BY THE GALTON INSTITUTE

British Library Cataloguing in Publication Data

Herbert Spencer : the intellectual legacy

  1.Spencer, Herbert, 1820-1903 - Congresses 2.
  Spencer, Herbert, 1820-1903 - Influence -
  Congresses
  I.Jones, Greta, 1943- II.Peel, Robert A.
  192

  ISBN 0950406686

First published 2004 by the Galton Institute, 19 Northfields Prospect, Northfields, London SW18 1PE

Printed and bound in Great Britain by The Chameleon Press, 5-25 Burr Road, Wandsworth, London, SW18 4SG

Contents

Notes on the Contributors

Naomi Beck, Universite de Paris (Pantheon-Sorbonne)

Dr Thomas Dixon, Churchill College, Cambridge

Professor Greta Jones, University of Ulster

Dr John Laurent, Griffith University, Queensland, Australia

Professor J.D.Y. Peel, School of Oriental and African Studies, University of London

Professor Robert J. Richards, Fishbein Center for History of Science, University of Chicago

Introduction

Herbert Spencer (1820-1903) and Francis Galton (1822-1911) were almost exact contemporaries. They were also professional associates and close friends. The nature of their friendship was recalled by Galton in his Herbert Spencer Lecture given in Oxford in June 1907[1] in which he acknowledged his personal debt to Spencer "which is large" and went on to describe the context of their relationship: "It was [our] custom for many afternoons to spend an hour or two of rest in the old smoking room of the Athenaeum Club strolling into an adjoining compartment for a game of billiards when the table was free. Day after day on those afternoons I enjoyed brief talks with him which were often of exceptional interest to myself."

Pearson,[2] amongst others, noted that at 42 Rutland Gate, Galton's home for 40 years, Spencer was prominent amongst the collection of prints of Galton's friends which decorated the walls of his dining room, where he also did his writing. Others were of Darwin, Grove, Hooker, Broderick and Spottiswoode.

This gallery of contemporaries was the pictorial representation of Spencer's "circle" described in the first chapter of this volume. Darwin was, of course, the centre of this unique constellation of talent – an assembly of intellectual abilities in a given time and place with few historical parallels – and Spencer and Galton each had a special relationship with the great biologist. W.F. Bynum portrays Galton as "one whose intellectual life utterly hinged on Darwin's work". He suggests that "without the sense of process which Darwin's work provided the whole thrust of his research after the mid-1860's is unimaginable".[3] Spencer, on the other hand, was an evolutionist, even a Darwinian, long before the *Origin of Species*. He made Darwin a gift of the very phrases by which the latter is generally remembered – "the survival of the fittest" and "the struggle for existence". It was in fact Wallace who urged Darwin to substitute "survival of the fittest" for "natural selection". "This term", he wrote to Darwin in 1866 "is the plain expression of the fact; natural selection is a metaphorical expression of it and to a certain indirect and incorrect sense, even personifying Nature, she does not so much select special variations as exterminate the most unfavourable ones".[4]   This substitution also, he might well have added, more clearly and properly acknowledges Malthus, to whom all three owed a considerable intellectual debt.   Galton, had he been consulted, may have taken the opposite view.

Bynum also reminds us that Galton's "career and contributions lay outside any notion of the professional, within an amateur tradition that did not recognise disciplinary boundaries and ... was all the richer for it".   Spencer's "theory of everything" specifically designed to ignore, in fact to destroy, all boundaries and to encompass ethics, metaphysics, biology, psychology and sociology within its overall evolutionary scheme whilst Galton was so wide-ranging in his interests as to be dubbed a dilettante.   Their endeavours, moreover, were practical as well as theoretical. Spencer invented the metal paperclip and Galton the *Times* weather-map and when Galton demonstrated to Spencer his use of the stereoscope in producing composite photographs he learned that his friend had attempted the same task by superimposing tracings of different individuals.   Both, moreover, were impelled to translate their highly abstract philosophical theories of society into practical and detailed utopian schemes. [5]

Sadly the sole attempt of these two nineteenth century scholars to work formally together was unhappy and short-lived.   In 1863 J.M.F. Ludlow, editor of *The Christian Socialist*, Charles Kingsley, the novelist and Thomas Hughes, author of *Tom Brown's Schooldays* founded a popular weekly magazine *The Reader* whose aim was to provide an organ of communication amongst scientists of different disciplines and between them and the public.   They established a triple editorship comprising Galton, Spencer and Norman Lockyer, a young astronomy student then earning his living as a clerk in the War Office.   This worthy early venture in the promotion of the public understanding of science lasted a mere three years before collapsing to the "multiple clashing of egos".   It has to be said, even in the context of a book such as this, that not all the fault lay with Galton and none at all with Lockyer.   However, out of the ruins of *The Reader* another periodical was launched with identical aims and with Lockyer as sole editor. Under the title *Nature* it went on to become the world's leading scientific journal. Lockyer, subsequently knighted and appointed to the chair of astronomical physics at the Royal College of Science, continued to edit *Nature* for the next fifty years.

Unable to work co-operatively, Spencer and Galton nevertheless found no difficulty in working apart. Their published output was, by any standards, before or since, prodigious. The complete list of Galton's writings takes up fifteen tightly printed pages in Forrest's biography,[6] whilst Spencer's resembles the quinquennial output of a full university department rather than one man.[7] Direct comparison between the two is difficult because whilst Galton wrote many journal articles, Spencer sought to ensure a more lasting posterity between hard covers. To be fair Spencer also needed the money that books generated but journal articles did not. Galton, though not so rich as his cousin, who had married into the Wedgwood wealth, had the means to live a comfortable independent life.

Their productivity had no doubt a firm grounding in the work ethic enjoined by their long discarded non-conformist upbringing. But beyond this their lives were organised to facilitate an undistracted commitment to strictly intellectual concerns. Neither had children; Spencer was a bachelor and Galton's marriage "appears to have been neither initiated nor sustained by any very strong passions".[8] And although both men did, apparently, have at least one real and severe nervous breakdown (as indeed did Mill and Darwin), their life-long hypochondria seems to have been little more than a convenient alibi enabling them to avoid social contacts and those engagements which they found uncongenial.

Fame and recognition came early and in abundance to both Galton and Spencer. Between his election to a fellowship of the Royal Society at the age of 34 and his knighthood (from a Liberal Government) in 1909 Galton was the recipient of every conceivable award from learned societies in England and abroad, including the Copley medal of the Royal Society and the gold medal of the Royal Geographical Society. Spencer was offered and rejected numerous honours including fellowships both of the Royal Society and of the British Academy. It has been suggested that Darwin was denied a state honour because of the challenge to religion which his writings implied. Yet Galton and Spencer who were unambiguously anti-religious – Spencer argumentatively so and Galton dismissively – incurred no such penalty.

Spencer enjoyed one accolade which escaped Galton and this was his immortalisation in *Vanity Fair*.

The familiar and instantly recognisable caricatures of statesmen, artists, writers and others which appeared weekly in *Vanity Fair* from 1869-1914 are today most often encountered mounted and framed as decorative prints in the offices and homes of politicians, lawyers, doctors, or mere aficionados of this art form.   When published each print was accompanied in the magazine by a pen profile of its subject and together the 2,300 portraits and biographies provide a colourful and unique insight into the political, social and intellectual life of the latter part of the nineteenth century.   The caricatures and biographies "became a record of Victorians and Edwardians interpreting each other and how they viewed themselves has, in turn, influenced later assessments of the eras".[9]

Spencer appeared in *Vanity Fair* on 26 April, 1879 and his caricature forms the frontispiece of this book. "C G" was the *nom de crayon* of Sir Francis Carruthers Gould (1844-1925). Most of the cartoons of *Vanity Fair* were drawn by Sir Leslie Ward ("Spy") or Carlo Pellegrini ("Ape") but guest artists (including Sickert, Whistler and Tissot) contributed from time to time. Gould was one of these and his drawing conforms to the familiar idiom of the series. Gould was the lead cartoonist of the *Westminster Gazette* and the sole illustrator of *Picture Politics*.   Although unsigned, the accompanying biography, reproduced here, was written by Thomas Gibson Bowles (1842-1922) who either anonymously or as "Jehu Junior" wrote every biography and much else in the magazine during the first twenty years of its existence.[10]

MEN OF THE DAY. No. 198.

MR. HERBERT SPENCER.

HERBERT SPENCER holds the present greatest name among the philosophers. He is scarcely known in his own country outside the circles of fogies, but abroad he enjoys a wonderful reputation as the leader of all modern thought. He was born nine-and-fifty years ago, the son of a schoolmaster, who strove to culture him with the classics, and to make of him a civil engineer. But young Spencer resisted Greek and Latin, and soon renounced engineering. He was, and knew himself to be, powerful with the pen; so he became a writer. He learnt to handle a good plain English of the frigid sort. In a casual way he published articles on Government, Education, and other dull subjects, from the time he was one-and-twenty. But when Darwin invented Evolution, Evolution invented Herbert Spencer, who saw how the notion might be applied to psychologic problems. So he now addressed himself to pure philosophy, and began to publish distressing tomes. He fell foul of Comte and of Mill, and plunged about with atoms and monads in such fashion as made all men see that be must have a philosophy of his own. As nobody could well understand him his reputation waxed mightily. He is now the one recognised authority on "Sociology;" he has discovered that "ultimate scientific ideas are all representatives of realities that cannot "be comprehended," and that the man of science "knows that in its ultimate essence nothing " can be known." Yet he goes on writing.

Mr. Herbert Spencer is believed by many to be a companionable, cheerful man. He has been more than once to a shareholders' meeting to war with railway directors; he delights also in children; and he holds that suicides should rather be encouraged. Yet he goes on living.

Facsimile of *Vanity Fair* pen portrait of Spencer, 1879

Surprisingly perhaps there is, in England, no Herbert Spencer society dedicated to marking his anniversaries and otherwise perpetuating his memory. It seemed appropriate in all the circumstances that The Galton Institute should stand proxy in this matter during Spencer's centenary year and the chapters in this book are based on papers given at a well-attended conference held in 2003 at The Linnean Society of London. The success of that event encourages us to believe that this volume will be similarly welcomed.

In planning the conference programme the Institute attempted to demonstrate the many fields in which Spencer's influence is still regarded as relevant and to bring together academics from three continents who are producing important new work on Spencer.

The 2003 Galton Lecturer, who contributes the final and forward-looking chapter of this book, suggests that a new life of Spencer is probably overdue. Since he himself is the author of the current definitive biography, his suggestion must be taken seriously. We believe that whoever undertakes that important task will find much in this volume of significance and help.

The Galton Institute is grateful to all those who gave papers at the 2003 conference and to Betty Nixon for her help in organising that meeting. The cover photograph of Spencer (1893) is reproduced by courtesy of The Linnean Society; the frontispiece is from the Institute's Treasurer's private collection of *Vanity Fair* prints.

Notes and References

1   "Probability: the Foundation of Eugenics", Sir Francis Galton *Essays in Eugenics*, London, Eugenics Education Society 1909 pp.72-99. Galton *wrote* this lecture and was present at its delivery but because he was recovering from a severe fall the lecture was read for him.

2   *Life, Letters and Labours of Francis Galton*, Vol. II p.11. Cambridge University Press, 1914-1930.

3   W.F. Bynum (1993) "The Historical Galton" in *Sir Francis Galton FRS: The Legacy of his Ideas*, Milo Keynes (Ed.) London: Macmillan for The Galton Institute.

4   Malcolm J. Kottler "Charles Darwin and Alfred Russel Wallace: Two Decades of Debate over Natural Selection" in David Kohn, ed., *Darwinian Heritage*, Princeton 1985, quoted in Carl N. Degler *In Search of Human Nature*, Oxford University Press, 1991, p.61.

5 The only remaining fragments of Galton's "Kantsaywhere" are reproduced in Pearson *op cit*; Spencer's utopian schemes are described in Part II of his *Sociology* p.594 ff.

6 D.W. Forrest, *Francis Galton: the Life and Work of a Victorian Genius*, London: Elek, 1974

7 A complete list of Spencer's publications is provided in J. Rumney *Herbert Spencer's Sociology*, London: Murray, 1934. If translations are taken into account Spencer is clearly ahead and of course has remained in print much longer than Galton.

8 J.H. Edwards "Francis Galton: numeracy and literacy in Eugenics" in Keynes, *op cit* p.81.

9 John Pope Hennessy stated that to have one's caricature in *Vanity Fair* was a "public honour no eminent man could well refuse". Quoted in Roy T Matthews and Peter Mellini *In Vanity Fair* Berkeley and Los Angeles: University of California Press and London: Scolar Press, 1982.

10 Bowles left *Vanity Fair* in 1889 and became an MP. He also founded a number of other periodicals including *The Lady,* which still survives to the present day. His eldest daughter married Lord Redesdale and became mother to the Mitford sisters.

1. Spencer and his Circle

Greta Jones

In 1866 George Grote (1794-1871), professor of classics and treasurer of London University, wrote to Alexander Bain about Bain's suggestion that Herbert Spencer be invited onto the Senate of the University of London. "How should I describe his merits to Lord Granville" he wrote, "as a physiologist, or psychologist or physical philosopher in general? What is his position in society? Has he any profession?"[1]

Having not traced the reply that Grote received to his query about Spencer, I propose to construct the answer for myself. The reply could well have been along these lines:

> He is a physiologist, psychologist and physical philosopher – though the last in the broadest sense. But you must also add to that he is an ethical philosopher, a sociologist, a political commentator and controversialist and has made some small but important contribution in biology. His profession is at present 'man of letters' sustained by a small independent income. His position in society was originally of the provincial middle class and he was brought up as a Methodist. However, he now works, lives and socialises among the intellectual classes of the metropolis particularly those who belong to the school of advanced liberal and radical views. Indeed it is with that in mind that I propose him to the Senate since our objective is to secure enough votes to keep out from the chair of moral philosophy a clergyman of whose views we particularly disapprove.[2] We can rely upon Spencer for that. By the 1870s I predict he will be even better known than yourself, and certainly myself, due to the wide popularity of evolution and, in particular, the self definition of the age as evolutionary. You yourself belong to an older radical tradition whose origins lie in the 18th century nurtured by utilitarianism.

This philosophy seems increasingly arid to the reading public of today. Since many among our middle classes believe the world to have changed – and for the better – they require the laws of that world to be explained to them. Spencer will be seen as precisely the person who has done that. Darwinism has shown this to be the question of the day and there are even some who think Spencer to be a more important figure and a superior philosopher to the great man himself.

***

Spencer was born in Derby in 1820 into a middle class family. There was a tradition of political radicalism in Derby and in a recent article Paul Elliot has demonstrated there was also a tradition of speculative evolutionary philosophy. In the latter case it was nourished by Erasmus Darwin who moved to Derby in 1781 and became part of its intellectual life particularly through his association with the Derby Philosophical Society founded in 1783.[3]

The characteristic politics of the urban middle class, especially those brought up outside the Church of England, were liberal verging on radical. To be a liberal in politics in the period from Spencer's youth till his maturity in the 1870s meant to be in favour of parliamentary reform, to embrace enthusiastically capitalist industrialisation and free trade, to desire the loosening of the links between the established church and British institutions including the Universities, to advocate meritocracy in the process of appointment to the army and civil service rather than patronage, to be suspicious of foreign adventures abroad, hostile to standing armies and pre-disposed to the peaceful resolution of international disputes. Apart from his growing religious scepticism, Spencer was a prime representative of this political culture. Those who have argued that his intellectual work can only be really understood as a conscious and sometimes unconscious defence of that form of urban civilisation have a strong point. It can be seen in Spencer's hostility to the state, his concomitant belief in the diffusion of power from the centre to the periphery, his conviction in the superiority of industrial over what he called militant society and his use of concepts such as the unintended but beneficial outcome of hundreds of thousands of self interested actions carried out without reference to each other – in other words the invisible hand of classical political economy.

As for his profession, outside of literature and journalism, the only paid occupation Spencer ever pursued was as an engineer for the railways from 1837 to 1846. Railway surveying also nurtured two other substantial figures of science in the nineteenth century who later became colleagues and friends of Spencer, Alfred Russel Wallace – the co-discoverer of the theory of natural selection – and John Tyndall the physicist and president of the Royal Institution. In all three cases the railways nourished in them an interest in geology, an appreciation of the extent and power of the industrial transformation taking place in the 1830s and 1840s and, indirectly, strengthened their evolutionary philosophy. In the 1840s all believed in some version of progressive change in the social and the natural world.

Spencer started his literary career around 1836 writing for the radical and nonconformist provincial press and occasionally for engineering journals. Spencer's political and economic writings brought him to the notice of the editors of national radical journals and launched his career in London. He moved to London on becoming sub editor on *The Economist* in 1848.[4]

However, Spencer's association with the *Westminster Review* and the circle around it was particularly important to his early career. Spencer had two articles in the first volume of the re-launched series in 1852 and it was, along with the *Leader*, his primary outlet for the publication of his journal articles throughout the 1850s and 1860s.

The *Westminster's* circulation was not great in comparison to other Victorian periodicals. In 1860 it sold around 4,000 copies, only half the circulation of periodicals such as *Fraser's*, the *Quarterly*, *Blackwoods* and the *Edinburgh* in that year. However, the publisher John Chapman, who took over the *Westminster* from John Stuart Mill in 1850, made it an important force in Victorian intellectual life. His association with Chapman and the *Westminster* also gave Spencer an entrée into London literary circles. Through Chapman he met the *avant garde* of London society including in 1851 Marion Evans – later to become the novelist George Eliot and the woman Spencer came closest to marrying.

Spencer's fame rose as a consequence of and in parallel with the revolution in publishing in the nineteenth century. This revolution has several facets. First was the increasing accessibility of books, which until then had been expensive, the private library being like the private menagerie – usually an index of wealth and aristocratic status. Books were still expensive in the nineteenth century but growing disposable income brought them increasingly within the grasp of the middle classes. This produced a predominantly middle class audience and, it must be said, a dominance of middle class taste.

As Jonathan Rose points out in the *Intellectual Life of the British Working Class*, in the early and mid nineteenth century, apart from a few standard texts, most books in working class homes were second hand, a phenomenon which produced a peculiar dislocation between middle and working class reading.[5] Only towards the end of the century, with the coming of large print runs which lowered the cost of books to the buyer, did Spencer's works become more widely available, including to better off working class readers. In the history of the diffusion of Spencer's ideas this is significant, producing at the end of the century when Spencer's star was beginning to diminish among the middle class reading public, a rise in interest in him in more plebeian circles.

Newspapers and periodicals also flourished in the nineteenth century – one estimate is that more than 25,000 newspaper and periodical titles were published during the reign of Victoria. Reading as a pastime, for entertainment as well as instruction, became more general. But it should be remembered that oral communication was still important. Newspapers published accounts of the proceedings of local societies and of national meetings. The most newsworthy and controversial of these could affect sales of newspapers, books and periodicals. Huxley's clash with Bishop Wilberforce over Darwin at the British Association in 1860 boosted interest in Huxley's published work. Tyndall's

Address at the British Association in 1874, which he used to great effect to challenge religious orthodoxy, is considered to have made John William Draper's *The Conflict between Science and Religion*, published the following year, a best seller.

Spencer was not a charismatic speaker like Huxley and, apart from his American lecture tour in 1882, did not exploit this particular route to literary celebrity; but he did become a celebrity.[6] Aiding him was the gradual abandonment of the convention of anonymity. Spencer did not sign his early articles for the *Westminster* but by the 1860s it had become common to append your name to your writings. In the close knit world of London intellectual life, anonymity was seldom real – your name was generally known – but with the growth of a much more extensive reading public, the abandonment of anonymity meant a celebrated name became a means to sell books.

Spencer's early literary endeavours, however, were not particularly well rewarded or famous. It was not easy to make a living by the pen in the nineteenth century, particularly for serious scientific work. Science and social philosophy were far-outstripped in popularity by the novel, travel, biography and theology. Only when a market for school science textbooks opened up at the end of the nineteenth century did scientific writing become profitable. The only book that made a modest profit for Spencer in the 1850s and 1860s, apart from the payment he received for periodical articles, was his book on *Education* in 1861. When Edward Youmans visited Spencer in 1862, Spencer told him "His books have never paid him anything but, on the contrary, have weighed him down like a millstone". 500 copies of the *Principles of Psychology* had been printed in 1855 and 300 remained on Spencer's hands seven years later. 750 copies of *Social Statics* published in 1851 had nearly all been sold – eleven years later. As far as his magnum opus was concerned "the whole thing would have been exploded this summer but for some means which he obtained from the death of an uncle".[7]

Spencer's magnum opus was the *Synthetic Philosophy*, which comprised five weighty treatises beginning with *First Principles* in

1862 and ending with the final volume of the *Principles of Ethics* in 1893.[8] It owed its existence to six hundred subscriptions to the series, which Spencer managed to gather. What his early writings did bring, however, was what the novelist Grant Allen, Spencer's disciple, called "success d'estime", a reputation which gave you access to influential intellectual circles and, hopefully, invitations to write for the better paying journals.

When Grote inquired from Bain about Spencer in 1866 it was because, outside certain circles, Spencer would not have been well known. But that situation was to change over the next few years. Spencer did become a celebrity known to the middle class reading public at large. The major reason was Spencer's association with the Darwin circle.

***

Spencer first met Huxley in 1852 and was introduced by him to Tyndall a year later. By the time of the publication of the *Origin* in 1859, Spencer was a colleague and confidante of two of Darwin's most crucial allies in the subsequent battles over evolution. He was one of the original members of the X Club founded by Huxley and Tyndall in 1864 – the only one, apart from John Lubbock (Lord Avebury) a Liberal MP from 1870, who was not a practising scientist in the sense in which we now understand that term.[9]

Spencer was embraced by this circle in the 1850s not just out of growing respect for his intellectual achievements, though this played a part. More significantly, Huxley's beliefs that theology must be expunged from scientific enquiry, the institutional ties between British universities and the churches weakened, and merit not religious orthodoxy become the basis for scientific advancement were all perfectly in line with Spencer's views. Like Spencer, Huxley saw the industrial transformation of Britain as the basis of Britain's economic strength and political freedoms.

Spencer was also an evolutionist, but in the 1850s this was of minimal concern to Huxley who, whilst he contemplated the possibility and even likelihood of evolution with equanimity, was not particularly convinced by the arguments of those who, hitherto, had applied the idea to biology. Some historians have argued convincingly that, even whilst the *Origin* may have made Huxley a thoroughgoing evolutionist, it did not make him a thoroughgoing natural selectionist.[10]

Nor was this the case with Spencer. After the publication of the *Origin*, Spencer's position within the Darwin circle was consolidated both by his evolutionism and his commitment to seeking the universal truths of nature through the application of scientific method alone. But Spencer tended to concede only a part for natural selection in evolution and only a minor part at that.

Whilst natural selection was debated in scientific and intellectual circles, as far as the general public were concerned it was not natural selection that Darwinism made popular but the general idea of evolution. Evolutionary ideas not based on natural selection – for example Lamarckism or use inheritance, which Spencer used as a foundation for his evolutionary theory – experienced, after the *Origin*, an upsurge in interest and popularity.

The controversy over Darwin made Spencer's own evolutionary ideas more significant and relevant. As part of the Darwin circle, associated in the minds of the public with the great protagonists of Darwinism, Spencer's name acquired added importance. He seemed to be the thinker who most exemplified the leading idea of the time, an idea which produced a wide imitative literature illustrating the ubiquity of evolution in society, psychology, politics, poetry, the colour sense, even church vestments.

Evolution was also entertainment. It provided dramatic confrontations at the British Association in 1860 and 1874, newspaper editorials, novels and plays, cartoons, jokes, conversation, family quarrels, political banter on the hustings, and side shows featuring "the missing link", "the ape man" and even "the variation".[11] Ultimately it ensured Spencer's transition from "success d'estime" to one of the most widely known authors of his time, able to make not a large but a modest living from writing.

This came about through the exploitation by publishers of the appetite for information about evolution which had been

quickened by the Darwin controversies.   Edward Livingston
Youmans was literary editor at the American publisher Appleton
and had read Spencer's *Principles of Psychology* (1855) in 1856 and
Social Statics (1851) in 1859. Youmans was a convert to Spencerian
evolution and sought out Spencer in a visit to England in 1862,
becoming his American literary agent. Through Spencer, Youmans
was introduced to members of the Darwin circle and the new
generation of scientists and evolutionary philosophers – Huxley,
Tyndall, Carpenter, Clifford, Balfour and Bain.   They also put
Spencer in touch with Darwin himself.   Appleton, through the
agency of Youmans, became the outlet for the works of Darwin
and the Darwin circle in the United States – aided by the fact that,
in the absence of copyright agreement between the United
Kingdom and America, they nonetheless were prepared to pay a
reasonable sum in royalties. These contacts were the genesis of the
famous *International Scientific Series*, published between 1871 and
1911, one of the most successful ventures in the popularisation of
science. Spencer, Huxley and Tyndall were invited to become the
advisors on the series and it was of great importance to the
Darwinians, not only for the financial benefits it brought but in the
intellectual influence it allowed them to exercise among the new
middle class reading public.[12]   In a recent article on the series,
Leslie Howsam claims that "Huxley and his colleagues wished to
revolutionise the dissemination of science in society, to reach a
much broader audience than before, an audience of readers who
could afford no more than five shillings a volume".[13]

Youmans' genius was that he devised the series of 120 books
around the concept of what constituted "modern thought", what
an educated person should consider it necessary to have on his or
her shelves to be considered well read and up to date. We should
not underestimate the influence of this. Thomas Hardy describes
in a novel written in 1892 *The Well-Beloved* his heroine's "regard of
herself as modern" which involved access to the culture and "new
education" which could be purchased at booksellers in every local
town.[14]

The importance of Youmans and the *International Scientific Series*
to Spencer was considerable. Together with Huxley and Tyndall he

was advisor to the series and, enthusiastically supported by Youmans, they made it a showpiece for late nineteenth century evolutionary thought. In addition evolutionary social thought and biological evolution were published side by side in the series, legitimising Spencer's search for a seamless web of concepts which embraced both. Social theory, in fact, generally sold better than more specialised scientific work published in the series, such as Huxley's *The Crayfish* (though Cooke's *New Chemistry* (1872) was also a best seller). Spencer's *The Study of Sociology,* published in 1873, sold over 26,000 copies followed by Draper and the economist Jevons's book on *Money,* both of which sold around the 20,000 mark.[15] The series also aided the increasing visibility of Spencer abroad. From the beginning Youmans planned to market the series across Europe as well as Britain and the United States and, with this in mind, he employed agents and translators in the major European countries.

Spencer's relationship to his readership is therefore quite complex. He was by the 1880s probably better known than actually read. Spencer's lifelong friend since 1844, the businessman Richard Potter, disconcerted him in the 1860s, when he asked Spencer to elucidate his principles "shortly" meaning in a short time. Spencer discovered that Potter, in spite of being regularly sent Spencer's books and having his opinions on them elicited, had not read any of them having, so he defended himself, "a rooted distrust of abstract ideas".[16]

It was the single works and periodical articles which were most read, though Spencer would have regarded these as merely a summary and distillation of his major intellectual contribution. People tended to know what Spencer represented – the triumph of the evolutionary idea – rather than have a close acquaintance with his actual arguments. Partly this can be put down to Spencer's own prose style, which his colleagues sometimes commented upon adversely. Those who ploughed through the synthetic philosophy were safe from the danger of "unnatural excitement", considered by the Victorians to be a possible source of harm arising from the growing popularity of the pastime of reading.[17]

To be an icon of the evolutionary movement had its downside. Grant Allen, in an essay on Spencer and Darwin in 1909, complained that over the years following the publication of the *Origin*, Spencer had gradually become second fiddle to Darwin. "It will probably be a great surprise to that large section of the public which habitually confines the idea of evolution to organic development and which believes Darwin 'invented' the theory of Descent with modification" but "Darwin did not originate the general idea of Evolution as a cosmical process"; that honour, Allen claimed, was Spencer's. The real relationship was: "To Herbert Spencer, Darwin was even as Kant, Laplace and Lyell, a labourer in a special field who produced results which fell at once into their proper order in his (Spencer's) wider synthesis".[18]

***

Spencer reached the peak of his fame in the eyes of his contemporaries in the 1870s and the mid 1880s. But thereafter his reputation diminished and the circles which had nourished him disintegrated. One reason was connected with developments within science. Spencer had underpinned his biology and psychology with the theory of use inheritance or inheritance of acquired characteristics, the most important formulation of which in the nineteenth century was that of Jean Baptiste Lamarck. In the 1880s the German experimental biologist August Weismann began a systematic assault upon Lamarkianism and the inheritance of acquired characteristics. Weismann's own contribution to the theory of heredity was eclipsed in the subsequent decade with the rediscovery of Mendel, but he certainly played a role in the history of biology in the revival of neo-Darwinism. Spencer considered that his biology and the psychological theories he had based upon his biology were under attack, particularly after Weismann was discussed at the British Association meeting of 1887. He felt obliged to defend the theory of use inheritance in the pages of the *Contemporary Review* 1893-94. Spencer's problem was that, having erected a comprehensive and interlocked system, criticism of one part of it threatened, he felt, to bring down the whole edifice of his synthetic philosophy.

But Spencer had to contend with a more general difficulty. By the end of the nineteenth century, the very success of Huxley in redefining the notion of a scientific career had the effect of marginalising the generalist and the amateur. Science was increasingly pursued as a profession, within the university or industrial research laboratory, by people who had acquired formal qualifications, often a university degree, and for whom expertise in one well defined and particular branch of science was the basis of subsequent advancement in their career. The biologist E. Ray Lankester wrote to Edward Clodd in 1909, in answer to a request for names of scientists who would contribute to a series on modern science, "The fact is that there are very few men of scientific repute who at present take up the attitude of Biologist or Historian. They are all busy on **special** lines and **economic** outcomes".[19]

Spencer published in *Mind*, *Nature* and the *Transactions of the Linnean Society* and he was proposed for election to the Royal Society in 1874 an honour he turned down because of his dislike of institutions which, to quote him, "hang on to the skirts of the titled class".[20] In other words he was embraced by the scientific community in his own day, an outcome he felt his due. But Spencer remained a generalist and amateur in science, his objective not scientific discovery as such but the general laws under which all branches of sciences could be systematised. To quote an ode which Grant Allen composed in Spencer's honour in 1874 his objective was to find "binding facts" and "unrelenting laws" all of which showed the "unity of cause". Spencer's individual scientific papers, whilst impressive in some cases, were intended primarily as illustrations of general law or to legitimise his philosophy by demonstrating his scientific knowledge and erudition.

Added to this was the passage of time, working upon the politics and ideologies of the latter half of the nineteenth century to Spencer's disadvantage. The Owenite socialist Alfred Russel Wallace had declared himself a follower of Spencer on his return from the Malay Archipelago in 1862. It was Spencer's social theory Wallace admired, not his biology, for Wallace rejected Lamarck and use inheritance much more emphatically than Darwin. The influence of Spencer can be traced in Wallace's article on social evolution of 1864.[21]   But Spencer's influence over Wallace depended upon the alliance between advanced radicals and the better off working class and trades union members, which was a political feature of the 1860s. The project, which looked viable in the 1860s, began to disintegrate in the 1870s and 1880s under the impact of economic depression and industrial militancy. This stimulated a debate about the limits of laissez faire and the need for more government intervention – a debate, it must be pointed out, carried on chiefly among middle class liberals rather than working class socialists. Spencer was alarmed about the political direction many opinion formers were now taking. The effect upon him was to induce him to formally repudiate the policy of land nationalisation – a traditional radical demand – because it might, in the changed context of the 1870s, be seen as giving succour to socialism and collectivism. The result was estrangement from Wallace.

More seriously for his position among the Darwinians, he came into conflict with Huxley. This happened first in 1871 when Huxley attacked those who criticised the Elementary Education Act of 1870 on the basis of "the dogmatic assertion that State interference beyond the limits of home and foreign police must, under all circumstances, do harm".[22] Huxley conceded that this "to my profound regret led me to diverge very widely from the opinion of a man of genius to whom I am bound by the twofold tie, to a profound philosopher and the affection given to a very old friend".[23] This divergence grew, however, over the next twenty years, ending with Spencer's resignation from the X Club and in a palpable coolness between him and Huxley, patched up somewhat towards the end of Huxley's life.

Political disagreement was one thing but in *The Man versus the State*, a series of articles in the 1880s attacking the growing collectivist sentiment among his contemporaries, Spencer made the fatal mistake in Huxley's eyes of using Darwin's name to argue the order of nature would be disrupted by greater state intervention. Huxley wanted the state to invest in scientific education and research. He did not belong to the school of "do nothings" as he called them. But mainly it was the presumption of Spencer in using

Darwin's name, his appropriation of it, which rankled. This was a direct challenge to Huxley's pre-eminent position as guardian of that name. The increasing acrimony between Spencer and Huxley had one positive outcome. It was among the factors leading Huxley to write *Evolution and Ethics* published in 1893, that classic statement of the naturalistic fallacy in social thought. Spencer described it pretty accurately as "a surrender of the general doctrine of evolution insofar as its higher applications are concerned".[24]

The sense that Spencer was falling from the prominence he had previously enjoyed – if not with the public at large certainly with that part of it which set the tone intellectually and politically – is encapsulated most poignantly in his relationship with the Potter family. He had singled out the daughter Beatrice, born in 1858, as the member of the family with the intelligence and energy to become his literary executor. But Beatrice also fell under the spell of the 1880s. In 1892 she married the Fabian socialist Sidney Webb, with whom in 1918 she was to draft the constitution of the Labour Party, including the most famous expression of collectivist ambition in British politics, clause four. Grant Allen, Spencer's most devoted acolyte, had also become a Fabian and so, in Spencer's eyes, disqualified himself from the task of literary executor. Spencer complained there was no one available to undertake the task "who possesses at once the literary gifts, the personal intimacy with my past life and the right opinions to undertake the task".[25]

In 1900 Spencer was famous. Accounts of the rise of evolution as an idea, of which there were a significant number still being produced, gave him an important place. But intellectual fashion was changing. The many imitations of the *International Scientific Series* which followed – the *Contemporary Science Series* and the *International Education Series* in 1889; the *New Progressive Science Series* in 1898; *Religions of the World* in 1904; *Philosophers Ancient and Modern* in 1908-10 – all pay tribute to the iconic status of evolution and to Spencer. But names such as Bergson, Schopenhauer, Nietzsche began to appear, all of whom attacked the notion of a determinant set of laws of evolution producing predictable outcomes.

In 1887 Beatrice Webb recorded in her diary a conversation she had with Huxley on the subject of Spencer. She "ventured to put forward the idea that Herbert Spencer had worked out the theory of evolution by grasping the disjointed theories of his time and welding them into one". Huxley dissented. In his view "Spencer never knew them: he elaborated his theory from his inner consciousness. He is the most original of thinkers, though he has never invented a new thought. He never reads, merely picks up what will help him to illustrate his theories. He is a great constructor: the form he has given to his gigantic system is entirely original; not one of the component factors is new but he has not borrowed them".[26]

This view does not altogether do justice to Spencer. For Spencer's contemporaries, the *Synthetic Philosophy* constituted his claim to originality and importance. Huxley and Spencer would have agreed on that. However, we do not necessarily read Spencer in the way he was read in the nineteenth century. We read his works partly because they are an important genealogy of the intellectual history of the nineteenth century. But within the corpus of his work are insights and arguments that still catch our attention for their intrinsic interest. Some are relevant to our own contemporary debates. The best introduction to the debate on the limits of the state is still Spencer's 1880s treatise *The Man versus the State* and it remains on philosophy and political science reading lists. The new biology has stimulated renewed interest in his psychology and ethics. His theory of international relations has still some considerable mileage. Even in his own time Huxley, trained, by Spencer himself, to look at the system forgot the individual contributions. Wallace's paper on Human Evolution of 1864 was in part inspired by *Social Statics*. Huxley's *Evolution and Ethics* was shaped by *The Man versus the State*. Darwin himself had many acknowledged and unacknowledged debts to Spencer.

Notes and References

1   Grote to Alexander Bain 18 November 1866: Robertson Papers, University College London, letter 61-3.

[2] This was the Reverend James Martineau, a prominent Unitarian.

[3] Paul Elliott "Erasmus Darwin, Herbert Spencer, and the Origins of the Evolutionary World View in British Provincial Scientific Cultures 1770-1850". *Isis* March 2003 vol. 94 number 1.

[4] He was introduced to James Wilson the editor by his uncle Thomas Spencer a prominent radical clergyman. The job was not particularly taxing giving him plenty of free time to write, rooms at the premises of the *Economist* at 340 the Strand and 100 guineas a year. See Ruth Dudley Edwards *The Pursuit of Reason. A History of the Economist 1843-1993.* London: Hamish Hamilton 1993.

[5] Jonathan Rose *The Intellectual Life of the British Working Class.* New Haven: Yale University Press 2001.

[6] In fact, accounts of his lecture in America point to a less than satisfactory experience for all concerned. Spencer, who had put off the trip on account of his health, "on landing was in so low a nervous state that the excitement of ordinary conversation was too much for him". *Herbert Spencer on the Americans and the Americans on Herbert Spencer. Being a full report of his interview and of the proceedings at the farewell banquet of November 9 1882.* New York: Appleton and Co. 1883. p. 5. He was "not practised in the arts of after dinner speech making and he was in certainly no condition to trust himself to impromptu remarks suitable to a festive occasion". He told them "As a life long student of social progress he did not think American society had reached the final stage of that progress – and he said so". *Ibid* pp. 6-7.

[7] John Fiske *Life and Letters of Edward Livingston Youmans* London: Chapman and Hall 1894 pp. 123-4.

[8] *Principles of Psychology,* published in 1855, was incorporated within the *Synthetic Philosophy* launched in 1862.

[9] The others, besides Huxley and Tyndall, were Lubbock, Busk ,Hirst, Frankland and Hooker. Later William Spottiswoode was added.

[10] For a discussion of this see Peter J. Bowler, *The Non-Darwinian Revolution. Reinterpreting a Historical Myth.* Baltimore: John Hopkins 1988 pp.76-8.

[11] Jane R Goodall. *Performance and Evolution in the Age of Darwin,* London: Routledge 2002.

[12] Works by British authors were often pirated in the United States until copyright law was changed in 1891. Appleton ensured reasonably generous commission on publication and sales.

[13] Leslie Howsam, "An Experiment with science for the nineteenth-century book trade;The International Scientific Series", *British Journal for the History of Science* vol.33 part 2 no.116 June 2000 pp. 187-207, pp192-3.

[14] Thomas Hardy *The Well-Beloved,* 1897 (serialised in *The Illustrated London News* 1892). Harmondsworth: Penguin Classics 1995 p. 13.

[15] In 1872 *Popular Science Monthly* was founded by Youmans. It also became a mouthpiece for the evolutionary views of Darwin, Huxley and Spencer.

[16] David Duncan. *Life and Letters of Herbert Spencer,* London: Methuen 1908 pp. 492-3.

[17] Kelly J Mays "The Disease of Reading and Victorian Periodicals" in John O Jordan and Robert L Patton (eds) *Literature in the Marketplace. Nineteenth- Century British Publishing and Reading Practices,* Cambridge: Cambridge University Press 1995.

[18] Grant Allen "Spencer and Darwin" *Fortnightly Review* 1896. Republished in *The Hand of God and Other Essays* London: Watts and Co. 1909 pp. 106 and 108.

[19] E. Ray Lankester to Edward Clodd 22 February 1909. Clodd Papers, University of Leeds

[20] David Duncan *op. cit.* p. 168.

[21] Wallace "The Origin of Human Races and the Antiquity of Man Deduced From the Theory of 'Natural Selection'" (1864) delivered to a meeting of the Anthropological Society of London on 1 March, 1864 and published in volume 2 of the *Journal of the Anthropological Society of London* 1864.

[22] "Administrative Nihilism" (1871) in T.H. Huxley, *Critiques and Addresses,* London: Macmillan 1883 p.10.

[23] *Ibid* p.iv

[24] Letter to James A. Skilton, 29 June 1893, in David Duncan *op. cit.* p. 336.

[25] Beatrice Webb, *My Apprenticeship,* (1926) Harmondsworth: Penguin 1971 p. 57.

[26] Webb's Diary. Entry of 6 May 1887. *Ibid.* p. 51.

2. The Relation of Spencer's Evolutionary Theory to Darwin's

Robert J. Richards

Our image of Herbert Spencer is that of a bald, dyspeptic bachelor, spending his days in rooming houses, and fussing about government interference with individual liberties. Beatrice Webb, who knew him as a girl and young woman, recalls for us just this picture. In her diary for January 4, 1885, she writes:

> Royal Academy private view with Herbert Spencer. His criticisms on art dreary, all bound down by the "possible" if not probable. That poor old man would miss me on the whole more than any other mortal. Has real anxiety for my welfare – physical and mental. Told him story of my stopping carthorse in Hyde Park and policeman refusing to come off his beat to hold it. Want of public spirit in passers-by not stopping it before. "Yes, that is another instance of my first principle of government. Directly you get state intervention you cease to have public spirit in individuals; that will be a constantly increasing tendency and the State, like the policeman, will be so bound by red-tape rules that it will frequently leave undone the simplest duties."[1]

Spencer appears a man whose strangled emotions would yet cling to a woman whose philosophy would be completely alien to his own, as Webb's Fabian Socialism turned out to be. Our image of Darwin is more complex than our image of Spencer. We might think of him nestled in the bosom of his large family, kindly, and just a little sad. The photo of him taken by Julia Cameron reveals the visage of an Old Testament prophet, though one, not fearsome, but made wise by contemplating the struggle of life on this earth. These images have deeply coloured our reaction to the ideas of each thinker. The pictures are not false, but they are cropped portraits that tend to distort our reactions to the theories of each. If we examine the major features of their respective constructions of evolution, we might be inclined, as I believe we should be, to recalibrate our antecedent judgements – judgements like those of Ernst Mayr, who in his thousand page history of biology celebrates Darwin over numerous chapters of superlatives but begrudges only three paragraphs to Spencer, "because his positive contributions [to evolutionary theory] were nil".[2] Mayr's attitude is reflected in most histories of science discussing evolutionary theory in the nineteenth century. Certainly nothing much of value can be expected from a boarding-house theorist.

Our contemporary evaluations of the ideas of Spencer and Darwin usually proceed, as Mayr's has, from the perspective of present-day science. Accordingly, Spencer's craft appears to have sunk without a trace, while Darwin's has sailed right into the port of modern biology. Our neo-Darwin perspective, I believe, adds to the distortion worked by our images of these Victorian gentlemen. During the latter part of his career, Spencer's star had certainly achieved considerable magnitude, such that his literary productions began actually to turn a nice profit. And his contemporaries recognised in his ideas comparable intellectual capital. Alexander Bain regarded him as "the philosopher of the doctrine of Development, notwithstanding that Darwin has supplied a most important link in the chain."[3] In the historical introduction to the *Origin of Species*, Darwin included Spencer as one of his predecessors; and he wrote to E. Ray Lankester that Spencer "will be looked at as by far the greatest living philosopher in England; perhaps equal to any that have lived".[4] Darwin's evaluations of Spencer would alternate between astonishment at the philosopher's cleverness and scorn at his inflated abstractions. Yet, the balance tipped heavily to the positive side. Darwin along with Thomas Henry Huxley, John Stuart Mill, Charles Babbage, Charles Lyell, Joseph Hooker, Alexander Bain, John Herschel, and a host of other scientists of rather less renown, subscribed to Spencer's program of "Synthetic Philosophy," which would issue volumes in biology, psychology, sociology, and morality. These Victorian coryphées redeemed Spencer's intellectual capital with real money. Grant Allen's admiration for Spencer's genius moved him to poetry:

Deepest and mightiest of our later seers,
Spencer, whose piercing glance descried afar
Down fathomless abysses of dead years
The formless waste drift into sun or star,
And through vast wilds of elemental strife
Tracked out the first faint steps of unconscious life.[5]

We may judge that Spencer got the poet he deserves, but we can hardly doubt that he made a significant mark on his contemporaries. His star, to be sure, was slow in rising and always included a reflective glow from Darwin's own. In what follows, I want to take the measure of Spencer's theory along three dimensions, which will allow comparison with essential features of Darwin's conception. These are: first, the origin and character of Spencer's general theory of transmutation, and then more specifically, the causes of species alteration and, finally, the particular case of human mental and moral evolution. In this comparison, I think we will find both some undervalued aspects of Spencer's scheme and some problematic aspects of Darwin's. But this reversal of fortune, if real, does produce an historiographic paradox: why the adulation of Darwin and the denigration of Spencer?

General Evolutionary Schemes

Both Darwin and Spencer eased into their evolutionary notions in pursuit of their early professions, and, indeed, aided by similar intellectual resources. Darwin, of course, sailed away on the *Beagle* to circumnavigate the globe, a journey that supplied the kind of experiences, recollected in the tranquillity of his London study, which led to the first formulations of his ideas about species descent. Those experiences, however, required the infusion of an ideational stimulant in order to crack the shell of orthodoxy. For Darwin, two works in particular, though hardly exclusively, provided the conceptual energy to give form to his experiences: Alexander von Humboldt's *Personal Narrative of Travels to the Equinocteal Regions of the New Continent,* which altered dramatically Darwin's view of nature, and Charles Lyell's *Principles of Geology,* which supplied the vast time scale and biogeographical suggestions for suspecting that Lamarckian transformation theory, which Lyell detailed in volume two of his work, might have much more to it than the author allowed.   And, of course, after Darwin had returned from the voyage, Thomas Malthus's *Essay on Population*, with its pregnant notion of population pressure, led Darwin to a "theory by which to work," as he himself expressed it.[6]

Spencer's early professional experience lacked the grand sweep of Darwin's.[7] As civil engineer in his late teens, he had his curiosity aroused by the many fossils he discovered while excavating new passages for the railroads. His reading of Lyell's *Principles of Geology* moved him, much as it had Darwin, to consider seriously the Lamarckian hypothesis. Lyell had, in the spirit of the Old Bailey, where he had trained as a barrister, presented a fair case for Lamarck's views, but assumed his subsequent refutation would nullify the theory completely. He was obviously too scrupulous in the former exercise and too hedging in the latter, at least for Spencer. Spencer, though, read few books to the end; so he may simply have missed Lyell's crucial closing arguments.   Less significant for Spencer than Darwin, however, were the fundamental biological aspects of development. Spencer was more interested in human social progress, and that was the consideration that lent the tipping weight to Lamarck's thesis.

Spencer's time with his uncle Thomas Spencer, a curate who had a definite political philosophy, kept him mindful of the possibilities of social development without the aid of government. Poor Laws, Spencer came to believe, were only devious instruments to arrest the need to deal with unjust distribution of the ultimate source of wealth, namely land. In his first book, *Social Statics*, published at his own expense in 1851, he sounded a call not unlike that of his contemporary, Karl Marx:

> All arrangements ... which disguise the evils entailed by the present inequitable relationship of mankind to the soil, postpone the day of rectification. A generous Poor Law is the best means of pacifying an irritated people. Workhouses are used to mitigate the more acute symptoms of social unhealthiness. Parish pay is hush money.   Whoever, then, desires the radical cure of

national maladies, but especially of this atrophy of one class and the hypertrophy of another, consequent upon unjust land tenure, cannot consistently advocate any kind of compromise.[8]

Only if government would step aside and allow natural development to take its course, Spencer suggested, could the society avoid armed insurrection.

Spencer sketched out that natural development of society in his book *Social Statics* and in his 1852 essay on *The Theory of Population*. Like Darwin, Spencer employed Malthus's notion of population pressure in a way antithetical to the parson's own dreary conclusions. Spencer argued that as populations grew, individuals would have to accommodate themselves to increasingly difficulty circumstances; habits would have to be developed to articulate men to these circumstances; and these habits, as well as the anatomical changes they would induce, would sink into the heritable structure of organisms, and so individuals would increasingly adapt to the requirements of society and eventually achieve perfect biological accommodation. This was a kind of utopian evolutionism, the goal of which Darwin himself would have acceded to – and, in fact, did, but only with a gaze beclouded with as much doubt as hope.

Spencer, in his essay, mentioned another feature of population pressure that echoes of Spencerian tragedy and Darwinian triumph. He wrote: "It is clear, that by the ceaseless exercise of the faculties needed to contend with them [i.e., the complexities of society], and by the death of all men who fail to contend with them successfully, there is ensured a constant progress towards a higher degree of skill, intelligence, and self-regulation – a better co-ordination of actions – a more complete life."[9] Thus the principle of natural selection oozed out of Spencer's Malthusian thought, but it immediately dried up. In later years, Spencer would point to this passage as indicating his claim to equitable partnership in authoring the theory of evolution that more and more became associated with Darwin's name.

The final aspect of his reconfiguration of Malthus is unadulterated Spencer. He relied on some very antique ideas, ultimately stemming from Hippocratic notions of pangenetic heredity. In ancient medical treatises, connections were made between the production of pangenes from various regions of the body, including the nervous system, and the reproductive organs. The Hippocratics imagined that seeds from all parts of the body, bearing the hereditary material, collected in the brain and slid down the spinal marrow to the generative organs. In the early modern period this ancient view gave rise to the notion that masturbation could cause insanity – a great expenditure of seed would virtually melt away the brain. Though Spencer may have been oblivious to the physiological theory behind the wobbly speculations of an ancient medical tradition, he added some loose causal observations of his own to propose an inverse ratio between biological conception and mental conception: the greater the mental complexity of the organism, the fewer the number of offspring. Hence, as human society progressed mentally toward perfection, population pressure should decrease. So Malthus's attempt to put the breaks on human improvement by reason of over population would be thwarted, at least theoretically, by Spencerian sexual frugality. Though Darwin wrote a complimentary letter to Spencer on receiving a copy of the essay on population, he did think that the principles of reproduction Spencer assumed were complete rubbish – after all, he did have his own large family as counter evidence.[10] But today, we know that Spencer was uncannily correct – greater mental work generally yields fewer biological progeny. The reasons for this, however, are not exactly those he supposed.

Spencer's socialist attitudes lost their vigour with age. By the 1890s, he averred that biological adaptation to the social state must diminish in force as the approach to perfect adaptation increased, so that only in infinite time would the utopia of his youthful radicalism be realised. And as his own modest wealth increased, he became considerably less enthusiastic about community ownership of land, finding individual ownership more equitable in the long run.

Natural Selection vs Functional Adaptations as Cause of Evolution

In his early writing on the development hypothesis, Spencer relied exclusively on habit and the inheritance of consequent anatomical modifications to explain adaptations. But with the publication of the *Origin of Species* in 1859, he came, as he admitted to Darwin, to appreciate the power of natural selection. In his letter of acknowledgement, he also mentioned to Darwin, lest it be overlooked, that he himself had advanced a similar idea, but confined his considerations to human improvement.[11]

In his book *First Principles*, published in 1860 and the initial volume in his series *Synthetic Philosophy*, Spencer relied on the idea of an equilibration between outer environmental circumstances and inner biological conditions in order to explain adaptations. The balancing adjustment of an organism would occur as it adopted new habits to deal with an altered environment. These habits would, in their turn, produce heritable anatomical changes and so realign the organism with its external circumstances. In his *Principles of Biology*, which he began issuing in fascicles in 1862, he had to recognise, however, two significant causes of adaptation, what he called "direct equilibration" – the Lamarckian idea – and "indirect equilibration," natural selection, or as he preferred to call it: "survival of the fittest."[12] He admitted that survival of the fittest could account for many traits of plants and the simpler accommodations of animals and men. But he stoutly rejected the suggestion that it could explain more complex co-adaptations. He illustrated his argument with the case of the great, if extinct, Irish elk. In order for its huge rack of antlers to have evolved, its skull must have thickened, its neck muscles strengthened, its vascular network enlarged, and its nervous connections increased. None of these traits, however, would be of any selective value without all of the others – large neck muscles, for example, would be useless without the great rack of antlers. Yet it would be highly improbable that all of these traits would have simultaneously appeared as spontaneous variations to be selected.[13] Their explanation, according to Spencer, had to be found in the gradual and mutual adjustment of different habits, which would ultimately instil co-adapted anatomical attributes. Later, in the 1880s, as the heat streaming from the ultra-Darwinians – such as Alfred Russel Wallace and August Weismann – began to be felt, Spencer elaborated his argument based on co-adaptation in a large, two part article *The Factors of Organic Evolution*, the aim of which was to show the insufficiencies of natural selection.[14] I note in passing that this is exactly the argument that contemporary advocates of Intelligent Design have attempted to rejuvenate with mouse glands and unleash as a new killer refutation of Darwinian evolutionary theory. Darwin himself answered this kind of objection – and Spencer specifically – when he spelled out, in his *Variation of Animals and Plants under Domestication,* how natural selection might operate to produce co-adaptations.   But the simple reply, which he also furnished, is that artificial selection can obviously produce the kind of co-adaptations that Spencer attributed solely to direct equilibration.   After all, multiple, mutual adaptations also go into the construction of pouter pigeons and sporting hounds.[15]

Wallace urged Darwin to replace the terms "natural selection" with Spencer's version "survival of the fittest."   He thought Darwin's terms too metaphorical and apt to mislead. As we know, Darwin demurred, saying that his original designation had become enmeshed so tightly within the fabric of the whole theory that it could not be extricated without confusion.   He did, though, mention Spencer's expression in the fifth and sixth editions (1869 and 1872) of the *Origin.*   I think Darwin was right to reject Spencer's alternative, since these two evolutionists were utilising completely different conceptions.   The difference hinged on the locus of the creativity of nature. For Spencer, survival of the fittest meant the elimination of inferior types; it was a negative process. The real creativity of nature, in Spencer's view, stemmed from functional adaptations and co-ordination through habit, with the inheritance of acquired characters moulding the structure of organisms. Moreover, survival of the fittest, Spencer emphatically maintained, did not mean survival of the better or the favoured. He urged that "very often that which, humanly speaking, is inferiority, causes the survival.   Superiority, whether in size, strength, activity, or sagacity, is, other things equal, at the cost of diminished fertility" – and here he harkened back to his population theory. He continued: "and where the life led by a species does not demand these higher attributes, the species profits by decrease of them, and accompanying increase of fertility ... Survival of the better does not cover these cases, though survival of the fittest does."[16] So, for Spencer, survival of the fittest meant, generally speaking, elimination of inferior traits, not the selection of favourable attributes and the building up of progressively better adaptations. The creativity of evolution, in Spencer's scheme, was left to Lamarckian functional accommodations. But for Darwin, natural selection was creative and produced better, more progressively advanced creatures.

Darwin's conception of the operations of natural selection had its germination in the theory of nature that he embraced during his *Beagle* voyage and that came to invest the *Origin of Species*. While on the voyage, he read and re-read the works of Alexander von Humboldt, particularly the young German's *Personal Narrative of Travel to the Equinoctial Regions of the New Continent*, an account of his journey to South and Central America in the years 1799 to 1804. Humboldt's understanding of the character of nature both in the large and in creatures stemmed from his engagement with various members of the early Romantic movement in Jena.[17] Humboldt depicted a nature pregnant with moral and aesthetic values, and governed by archetypal relationships. It was a nature open both to scientific articulation and to artistic intuition, each complementing the other. The ordering of Humboldt's cosmos did not come from a personal Creator, but from the fecund and intelligent resources of nature herself. Spinoza, a favourite philosopher of the German Romantics, had epitomised this view with the phrase "Deus sive natura" – God and nature were one. During the *Beagle* voyage, Darwin absorbed this depiction and rendered in his account of his journey nature much after the manner of the German Romantics. He reflected on his debt to Humboldt during his return voyage back to England, when he wrote in his Diary:

> As the force of impression frequently depends on preconceived ideas, I may add that all mine were taken from the vivid descriptions in the Personal Narrative

which far exceed in merit anything I have ever read on the subject.[18]

In the 1840s, when Darwin was attempting to formulate for himself the character of natural selection, he employed a potent metaphor. He likened the operations of selection to an all-powerful being:

Let us now suppose a Being with penetration sufficient to perceive differences in the outer and innermost organisation quite imperceptible to man, and with forethought extending over future centuries to which with unerring care and select for any object the offspring of an organism produced under the foregoing circumstances; I can see no conceivable reason why he should not form a new race (or several were he to separate the stock of the original organism and work on several islands) adapted to new ends. As we assume his discrimination, and his forethought, and his steadiness of object, to be incomparably greater than those qualities in man, so we may suppose the beauty and complications of the adaptations of the new race and their differences from the original stock to be greater than in the domestic races produced by man's agency.[19]

Here Darwin, through a telling trope, worked out for himself the character of the operations of natural selection: it acted with "forethought," designing adaptations, not simply of utility, but of aesthetic beauty as well. When this same creature made its appearance in the *Origin of Species* fifteen years later, it had shed some of its garb, but none of its deep vitality and moral temper:

Man can act only on external and visible characters: nature cares nothing for appearances, except in so far as they may be useful to any being. She can act on every internal organ, on every shade of constitutional difference, on the whole machinery of life. Man selects only for his own good; Nature only for that of the being which she tends ... It may be said that natural selection is daily and hourly scrutinising, throughout the world, every variation, even the slightest; rejecting that which is bad, preserving and adding up all that is good; silently and insensibly working whenever and wherever opportunity offers, as the improvements of each organic being in relation to its organic and inorganic conditions of life.[20]

Through means of a literary device, an aesthetic instrument, Darwin infused his conception of nature with "the stamp of far higher workmanship" – higher than any human contrivance could evince. Natural selection, in Darwin's image-driven language, patently displayed attributes that Spencer would have denied. Nature did not destroy, rather she creatively directed development in an altruistic and progressive way: "as natural selection works solely by and for the good of each being, all corporeal and mental endowments will tend to progress toward perfection," says Darwin in the *Origin*.[21] Darwin's notion of natural selection as a dynamic, creative force instilling value into nature undoubtedly has had a subtle, even preconscious appeal to the readers of the *Origin*, satisfying a deep need to find some solace in a world from which a creator God had fled. Spencer, by contrast, left his readers with a colder, darker view of the destructive power of nature.

Human Mental Evolution

Spencer initially worked out his theory of evolution in light of his utopian socialist vision – a gradual accommodation of human beings to the requirements of social living, so that the greatest amount of intellectual and ethical satisfaction might be achieved. Mental evolution was thus a principal concern right from the very beginning of his evolutionary theorising. The first book of his to achieve some public attention was the *Principles of Psychology*, published in 1855. Spencer had outsized aspirations for this treatise. He predicted that his book would achieve the same intellectual prominence as Newton's *Principia* – at least he so confided this hope to his father.[22] He believed he had resolved a dispute between the followers of Locke and those of Kant – a dispute then at the boil in the exchanges between John Stuart Mill and William Whewell on the status of universal knowledge claims. The Lockeans maintained that all knowledge was acquired from experience, while the Kantians held that some propositions of universal and necessary modality were innate and determinatively valid. In his *Principles of Psychology*, Spencer argued in Solomonic fashion and came to a conclusion that many philosophers and psychologists today – especially those travelling under the name of "evolutionary psychologist" – would endorse. He asserted that certain ubiquitous relationships in the experience of our ancestors concerning space, time, and causality had become impressed on their nervous systems, and rendered heritable by dint of constant impregnation. So today those epistemological connections would stand as intrinsic mental structures and serve as the foundation for *a priori* propositions in mathematics and physics. Spencer thus offered an evolutionary Kantianism as the revolutionary account for the foundation of the sciences.

Spencer sent Darwin a copy of his *Principles of Psychology* in early 1856, undoubtedly because he had heard from his friend Huxley that the reclusive naturalist was also working on descent theory.[23] Darwin's marginalia indicate he certainly read the book, if without deep penetration. He never mentioned Spencer's work in the early editions of the *Origin* or in the *Descent of Man*, where, in this latter, he revealed his own theories of human mental evolution. Just after the publication of the *Descent,* Spencer wrote his American promoter Edward Youmans to complain: "As no one says a word in rectification, and as Darwin himself has not indicated the fact that the *Principles of Psychology* was published five years before the *Origin of Species*, I am obliged to gently indicate this myself."[24] The message finally got home to Darwin, and in the last edition of the *Origin,* in 1872, he altered a concluding passage to say: "Psychology will be securely based on the foundation already well laid by Herbert Spencer, that of the necessary acquirement of each mental power and capacity by gradation." Despite Darwin's appraisal of Spencer, he seems to have been little directed by Spencerian ideas, nor was Spencer greatly influenced by Darwinian notions on questions of mental evolution. Both, nonetheless, developed closely parallel conceptions.

As early as the 1840s, Spencer had proposed that the continued development of society and the slow adaptation of its members to the social state would produce "mental and moral and through them, the social perfection of the human race."[25] When he began constructing his Synthetic Philosophy some twenty years later, he retained the conception of the evolutionary process in nature culminating in the moral perfection of human beings: his assessment of cosmic evolution in the initial volume of his system, his *First Principles*, and of biological, psychological, and social evolution in subsequent volumes – these all had the purpose of grounding a science of morals in evolutionary processes. He brought his system to a close in 1893 with the publication of his *Principles of Ethics*.

A comparable trajectory can be made out for Darwin. Though his initial thoughts were directed to animal adaptations, he quickly swung to the notion that the highest activity of the human animal – moral behaviour – had to be given account by his new theory. His early M and N notebooks, and his so-called "Old and Useless" notebooks, kept from 1837 to 1840 – all of these contain reading notes and theorising about human mental and moral transformation, leavened with recollections of his recent experience of the behaviour and mental condition of the South American Indians, the Fuegians and the Indians of the Pampas. During the despicable effort of the Spanish to exterminate the Indians of Argentina, Darwin detected noble and altruistic behaviour exhibited by individuals whom the colonials regarded as little better than animals. And the Indians exhibited moral courage without benefit of the Christian religion. Darwin thought his theory could explain such behaviour; and he felt the urgency to do so, lest a crack be left open for the Divinity to creep back into biology.

As Darwin worked out his early theory of moral evolution, he stumbled across a problem that threatened his account, not only of human behaviour, but also of his entire theory. This was the difficulty of the social insects – ants, bees, and termites. Soldier bees, for example, would sacrifice their lives for the welfare of the hive, yet since they were neuters, their behaviour could not be inherited by their offspring; moreover, even if they could reproduce, such altruistic behaviour would have the same effect as if they were neuters – dead bees don't leave progeny. Hence, natural selection could not, it seems, explain the altruistic behaviour of such insects. Darwin worried about this potentially crucial objection to his theory right through the late 1850s. But just before the publication of the *Origin,* he hit upon the solution: natural selection would operate on the entire hive or community of insects. Hence, those hives that by chance had members exhibiting altruistic behaviour would have a selective advantage, and their members, who would include the relatives of the self-sacrificial soldiers, would survive to propagate another day.[26]

Darwin's solution to the problem of the social insects became the model for his explanation of human moral behaviour in the *Descent of Man.* The explanation was elegant and one that many of us would still endorse. He wrote:

> It must not be forgotten that although a high standard of morality gives but a slight or no advantage to each individual man and his children over the other men of the same tribe, yet that an advancement in the standard of morality and an increase in the number of well-endowed men certainly give an immense advantage to one tribe over another. There can be no doubt that a tribe including many members who, from possessing in a high degree the spirit of patriotism, fidelity, obedience, courage, and sympathy, were always ready to give aid to each other and to sacrifice themselves for the common good, would be victorious over most other tribes; and this would be natural selection.[27]

Though he focused on human moral acts as that kind of behaviour most elegantly explained by his theory of community selection, he found the model to be generalisable. It could also explain growth in human intelligence. A tribe that by chance had a primitive Newton in its midst would profit by adopting his inventions and conceptual notions. This would give the tribe an advantage in competition with other tribes and so it would be selected, along with that ersatz Newton's relatives.[28] Again, mental traits that might not seem to be greatly advantageous to an individual might yet be selected at the community level and thus continue to advance.

Though Spencer retained the notion that complex traits of organisms – including complex moral behaviour – required a theory of direct equilibration for their explanation, he yet yielded to the attractions of Darwin's notion of community selection, so powerful was it. In the first part of his *Principles of Ethics*, which was initially published as *Data of Ethics* in 1879, Spencer distinguished two levels of altruism: one kind directed to the family and another to the larger society. He obviously found Darwin's conception of community selection, now narrowed to the family, a fit explanation for altruistic advantage given to children and more remote relatives. He yet held that self-sacrificial behaviour operating for the benefit of the larger society could only be explained by gradual accommodation to the social state – his long standing explanation dependent on direct inheritance of social characters. He perhaps recognised that group selection on unrelated individuals would not yield heritable advantage. Darwin, by contrast, came to believe that group selection *per se* could occur even without individuals being related.[29] The problem of group selection still bedevils modern biology.

Darwin's account of human morality largely depended on his theory of community selection, while Spencer's still fell back on the inheritance of acquired characters. Yet Darwin could as easily revert to direct inheritance when the situation demanded. This was the case when he focused on the problem of man's big brain. Wallace had pointed out that for sheer survival, humans needed a brain hardly larger than that of an orang-utan, that is, about the size, as Wallace suggested – about the size of that of the average member of a British gentleman's club. But if a large brain were not needed for survival, what accounted for the superfluous cerebral matter that most humans carried around? Darwin, after reading some recent German literature, concluded that our acquisition of language moulded the brain into more complex patterns, which would become heritable over time. Thus the human brain would grow with the complexity of language.[30] This kind of Darwinian position, though we might cavil about it today, yet reveals that deeper truth which both Spencer and Darwin recognised: namely, that human evolution takes place in society and that social relations become inscribed in the development of the individual.

It has sometimes been suggested that the phrase "social Darwinism" – a phrase that carries a large negative valence – be altered to the more historically correct "social Spencerianism," as if Darwin himself should be exonerated of any application of evolutionary theory to human beings. This suggestion obviously lacks all merit. Neither Darwin nor Spencer thought the human animal exempt from evolutionary understanding and consequent theoretical construction.

Conclusion

Darwin and Spencer relied on the same devices to explain human mental and moral evolution – that is, natural selection and direct inheritance of acquired relations. Each, however, emphasised that causal account about which each felt most proprietary – certainly no surprise there. No contemporary biologist would, though, be thoroughly satisfied with the theories of either one. Neither Spencer nor Darwin had, by our contemporary lights, a decent notion of heredity. Darwin had no problem, for instance, with natural selection operating on acquired characters; and, of course, his theory of pangenesis was designed to accommodate a Lamarckian kind of inheritance. Yet, we are all neo-Darwinians, but none of us would admit to being a neo-Spencerian (though we might charge our enemies with that). Why the denigration of Spencer and the apotheosis of Darwin? Let me conclude with a few suggestions as to the answer to this question.

First, I believe it is the intuitively clear idea of natural selection – at least in its later formulations – that we admire. Ernst Haeckel was ready to regard natural selection as analytically true and thus an immovable rock upon which to build evolutionary biology. Of course, Karl Popper also regarded it as analytically true, but drew a different conclusion as to its status in science. Darwin's own original conception, though, gave natural selection properties – namely its creative function – to which we are, I believe, inclined to be more favourably disposed than to the idea of negative elimination. This, I believe, is a second reason for the prospering of Darwin's fortunes.

One cannot dismiss a related aspect of Darwin's evolutionary views. They seemed to be based on large and disparate accumulations of empirical evidence. Though there is some illusion in this assumption, since the *Origin of Species* makes almost no use of that kind of empirical evidence we today would normally regard as demonstrative, namely the fossil record. Indeed, Darwin's first German translator, Heinrich Georg Bronn, levelled as a most potent objection to Darwin's theory that he offered only a possible scheme of species descent but lacked empirical evidence for the actuality of species descent.[31] Bronn had a point. The *Origin of Species* is filled with a great variety of stories about how life might have evolved. And so powerful are they, readers have been led simply to accept them as quasi-proofs that life has actually evolved. What Darwin does show is that the kinds of facts with which a naturalist would be familiar all hang together in unexpected ways when viewed through the lens of his theory. Spencer's leaden prose could not accomplish the same linguistic magic as Darwin's metaphorical and image filled writing.

A fourth reason for the ascendancy of Darwinism is that Thomas Henry Huxley and G.E. Moore indicted Spencer's evolutionary ethics with the charge of committing a great fallacy – the so-called "naturalistic fallacy," that because we have, as *a matter of fact*, evolved to regard certain actions as good or bad, we therefore *ought* to regard them as good or bad. Neither Huxley nor Moore appeared to notice that Darwin himself had committed, from their point of view, the same fallacy. As for myself, though, I think it's not a fallacy, but that's irrelevant here.[32]

A fifth reason for the low estimate of Spencer's programme surely has to do with his notions about the liabilities of government interference in natural processes of human development; those notions do run counter to most academically liberal sensibilities. Darwin made few preachments about the role of government, especially since his own social position seemed fairly much in harmony with the status quo of his society.

Finally, there are those indelible portraits of the sour bachelor and the prophetic sage. They do work on the imagination.

There is no chance that suddenly a place will be made for Spencer in the pantheon of great scientists. But a more historically sensitive reading might remove him from the lower depths where he now resides. His impact was felt throughout the nineteenth and early twentieth centuries, often in surreptitious ways, as Naomi Beck shows in her paper. He certainly deserves more than the three paragraphs granted him by Ernst Mayr.

Notes and References

[1] Beatrice Webb, *The Diary of Beatrice Webb: Volume one 1873-1892*, ed. Norman and Jeanne Mackenzie (Cambridge: Harvard University Press, 1982), pp. 127-28.

[2] Ernst Mayr, *The Growth of Biological Thought* (Cambridge: Harvard, 1982), p. 386.

[3] Alexander Bain to Herbert Spencer (17 November 1863), Athenaeum Collection of Spencer's Correspondence, MS 791, no. 67, University of London Library.

[4] Charles Darwin to E. Ray Lankester (15 March 1870), in *Life and Letters of Charles Darwin*, ed. Francis Darwin, 2 vols. (New York: D. Appleton, 1891), 2: 301.

[5] Grant Allen to Herbert Spencer (10 November 1874), Athenaeum Collection of Spencer's Correspondence, MS 791, no. 102, University of London Library.

[6] Charles Darwin, *The Autobiography of Charles Darwin*, ed. Nora Barlow (New York: Norton, 1969), p. 120.

[7] I have discussed Spencer's intellectual development in my *Darwin and the Emergence of Evolutionary Theories of Mind and Behavior* (Chicago: University of Chicago Press, 1987), chaps. 6 and 7.

[8] Herbert Spencer, *Social Statics, or the Conditions Essential to Human Happiness Specified, and the First of them Developed* (London: Chapman, 1851), p. 316.

[9] [Herbert Spencer], "A Theory of Population, deduced from the General Law of Animal Fertility," *Westminster and Foreign Quarterly Review* 17 (1852): 500.

[10] Charles Darwin to Charles Lyell (25 February 1860), in *Correspondence of Charles Darwin*, ed. Sidney Smith et al, 13 vol. to date (Cambridge: Cambridge University Press, 1985-), 8: 109-110: "I have just read his Essay on population, in which he discusses life & publishes such dreadful hypothetical rubbish on the nature of reproduction."

[11] Herbert Spencer to Charles Darwin (22 February 1860), in *Correspondence of Charles Darwin*, 8: 98-99.

[12] Spencer used the phrase "survival of the fittest" for the first time in his *Principles of Biology*. He introduced the term in a quite casual way, suggesting that only later it occurred to him as a felicitous expression. See Herbert Spencer, *Principles of Biology*, 2 vols. (New York: D. Appleton, 1866), 2: 53: "natural selection will favour the more upright growing forms: individuals with structures that lift them above the rest, are the fittest for the conditions; and by the continual survival of the fittest, such structures must become established."

[13] *Ibid.*, 1: 445-57.

[14] The articles were drawn together in a small book. See Herbert Spencer, *The Factors of Organic Evolution* (London: Williams and Norgate, 1887).

[15] Charles Darwin, *Variation of Animals and Plants under Domestication*, 2nd ed., 2 vols. (New York: D. Appleton, 1899), 2: 327-29, and 327n.

[16] Herbert Spencer, "Mr. Martineau on Evolution," in *Recent Discussions in Science, Philosophy, and Morals*, 2nd ed. (New York: D. Appleton, 1882), pp. 339-40.

[17] I have discussed the early German Romantic movement and Humboldt's particular views in my *The Romantic Conception of Life: Science and Philosophy in the Age of Goethe* (Chicago: University of Chicago Press, 2002).

[18] Charles Darwin, *Beagle Diary*, ed. R. D. Keynes (Cambridge: Cambridge University Press, 1988), p 443 (September 1836). These remarks were reprinted in Charles Darwin, *Journal of Researches into the Geology and Natural History of the Various Countries Visited by H. M. S. Beagle* (London: Henry Coburn, 1839), p. 604.

[19] Charles Darwin, "Essay of 1844," in *The Foundations of the Origin of Species*, ed. Francis Darwin (Cambridge: Cambridge University Press, 1909), p. 85.

[20] Charles Darwin, *On the Origin of Species* (London: Murray, 1859), pp. 83-84.

21 *Ibid.*, p. 489.

22 David Duncan, *Life and Letters of Herbert Spencer*, 2 vols. (New York: D. Appleton, 1908), 1: 98.

23 Darwin's note of thanks for the book (11 March 1855) is in *Correspondence of Charles Darwin*, 6: 56.

24 Herbert Spencer to Edward Youmans (5 June 1871), in *Life and Letters of Herbert Spencer*, 1: 197.

25 Herbert Spencer, "Leter VII," *Nonconformist*, 19 October 1842.

26 I have given an account of Darwin's crucial difficulty with the social insects in my *Darwin and the Emergence of Evolutionary Theories of Mind and Behavior*, pp. 142-52.

27 Charles Darwin, *Descent of Man and Selection in Relation to Sex* (London: Murray, 1871), 1: 166.

28 *Ibid.*, p. 161.

29 In the final edition of the *Origin of Species* (1872), Darwin invokes group selection quite clearly: "In social animals it [natural selection] will adapt the structure of each individual for the benefit of the community; if the community profits by the selected change." See *The Origin of Species by Charles Darwin: A Variorum Text*, ed. Morse Peckham (Philadelphia: University of Pennsylvania Press, 1959), p. 172.

30 See my "The Linguistic Creation of Man: Charles Darwin, August Schleicher, Ernst Haeckel, and the Missing Link in Nineteenth-Century Evolutionary Theory," in *Experimenting in Tongues: Studies in Science and Language*, ed. Matthias Dörries (Stanford: Stanford University Press, 2002), pp. 21-48.

31 In the translator's epilogue to the German version of the *Origin*, Bronn argued that Darwin had only shown that the kind of transformationism he advocated was possible but that he had not shown that it was actual. See H. G. Bronn, ASchlusswort des Übersetzers,@ in Charles Darwin, *Über die Entstehung der Arten im Thier- und Pflanzen-Reich durch natürliche Züchtung, oder Erhaltung der vervollkommneten Rassen in Kampfe um=s Dasyn*, (based on 2nd English ed.), trans. H. G. Bronn (Stuttgart: Schweizerbart=sche Verhandlung und Druckerei, 1860), pp.. 495-520.

32 I discuss the logic of evolutionary ethics and the naturalist fallacy in the second appendix to my *Darwin and the Emergence of Evolutionary Theories of Mind and Behavior*.

3. The Diffusion of Spencerism and its Political Interpretations in France and Italy*

Naomi Beck

The choice to study the diffusion and political interpretations of Spencerism can be justified in a number of ways. First, the nature and objectives of Herbert Spencer's life project, his *System of Synthetic Philosophy* (1862-1893), show it to be, above all, a political enterprise. Indeed, his extensive efforts to unify biology, psychology, sociology and ethics under the universal law of evolution had a dominant motive: providing the ideology of *laissez-faire* liberalism with scientific legitimacy. It was the "end-product" that fashioned and directed the development of the various parts of his system, rather than the other way around. The decision to examine the political interpretations of Spencerism is, therefore, the choice to focus on a central feature in Spencer's own thought.

Furthermore, Spencer enjoyed an immense and almost unparalleled popularity. It was overshadowed by the decline of Lamarckism in the late nineteenth century and the growing authority of evolutionary theories based solely on the principle of natural selection, which have become the predominant paradigm in the field. Since Spencer's biology relied on the Lamarckian principle of inheritance of acquired characteristics, the weakening of Lamarckism shook the very foundations of his whole system: his psychology, sociology, politics and ethics simply lost their *raison d'être*. This may account for the fact that historians and philosophers of science alike have shown little interest in the study of Spencerism, be it from a scientific or an ideological point of view.

But even though Spencer's glory was only ephemeral, it would be a mistake to overlook the profound impact of his theory. A little over a century ago, Spencer was one of the most influential writers in most industrial countries. His work was translated into many languages and had a very large circulation on both sides of the Atlantic. In fact, within Spencer's lifetime some one million copies of his books were sold and he counted amongst his admirers people from many different fields of study. Few individuals in the history of modern Western thought can be said to have had equal success. Therefore, in spite of the fact that Spencer's biological theories were largely discredited during the twentieth century, his influence on late nineteenth century thought was so profound that it merits serious attention.

The choice to compare France and Italy is the fruit of a number of considerations. First of all, in these two countries the language spoken is different from that in which Spencer's ideas were primarily formulated. It is not the case, for example, in the United States. Their comparative study offers, therefore, a good opportunity to analyse the crucial role played by publishers and translators in the process of diffusion. More important yet is the fact that in the late nineteenth century, study in these two countries underwent cardinal transformations. In France, after the defeat of 1870 and the proclamation of the Third Republic, the country entered a period of political, social and moral crisis. Scientific theories, notably evolutionary ones, took an active part in the general debate over the ideology of the new regime and other issues concerning the "social problem" and industrial growth. In Italy as well, after the completion of the *Risorgimento,* there was a strong battle between the monarchists and the republicans as to the political identity of the newly unified national territory. This "redefinition" took place mainly in opposition to the pontifical polity. And again we find Spencerism, alongside the then-regnant philosophical positivism, as a chief component of certain political doctrines.

In order to grasp the dynamics in the process of appropriation of Spencerian ideas – especially in the political arena – it is essential to understand the historical context in which they were diffused. Indeed, any given theory is inevitably interpreted on the basis of the audience's prior beliefs and attitudes. Spencer, like his fellow thinkers, elaborated his system of concepts with the aide of existing scientific theories, social models, moral ideas and religious and political doctrines. When his readers in France and Italy became acquainted with his work they discussed, naturally, the distinctive features of Spencer's synthesis, yet it was more the manner in which Spencerism was related to their own theories that interested them.[1] In this way, different cultural structures, different *mentalités*, with oftentimes disparate interests, came into contact.

The object of this article is to offer preliminary results of ongoing research that purports to explain why Spencerism was so successful in France and Italy and how it inspired diverse socio-political doctrines as the context changed. Starting with France, I will, for each country, examine the first references to Spencer's philosophy, the important vehicles for its diffusion and the high points in this process. I will then focus on two political interpretations of Spencer's socio-biology: the doctrine of "Solidarisme" as formulated by Léon Bourgeois and the doctrine of Scientific Socialism as constructed by Enrico Ferri. Their study will shed light on a rather atypical connection between Spencer's philosophy and Left-wing ideologies.

Professor Enrico Ferri (1856-1929)

I

The history of the diffusion of Spencerism in France is intimately related to the history of the positivist movement. When Spencer's writings were first discussed there they were perceived as yet another phase in the ongoing debate between positivism and spiritualism. Spencer was then considered as a younger version of J.S. Mill, or what Auguste Comte's disciples, like Emile Littré, viewed as pale English imitations of their mentor that threatened the French monopoly over positivism[2]. It is not surprising, therefore, that the first written reference to Spencer's philosophy in France was made by a spiritualist, Auguste Laugel, and not by a positivist.

Laugel's article from 1864 was dedicated to reviewing the state of philosophical studies in Great Britain and, more precisely, Spencer's philosophical project as it was exposed in First Principles.[3] He began his review by lamenting the sorrowful state of "sterile" English philosophy, despite the industrial supremacy of the country and its highly developed political and social institutions. In Great Britain, claimed Laugel, the contempt for metaphysics was so high that it became a doctrine in itself. The reason for this lack of "philosophers and philosophy" was to be found in a certain trait of the English character: the incapacity for abstraction, generalisation and systematisation. Fortunately, "in the midst of the universal indifference, Mr. Spencer remained steadily attached to his philosophical studies, displaying all the heroic courage and that rare independence indispensable to those who devote themselves to toilsome researches".[4]

What made Laugel so enthusiastic about Spencer's philosophy was his *Plan for a System of Synthetic Philosophy*, announced in March 1860. Spencer's project was "grand" and "audacious" and its scope "the vastest one could conceive. It embrace[d] all of the sciences as well as the whole of metaphysics". It took no less than the "fertility of [a] genius, and almost encyclopaedic knowledge" exclaimed Laugel, to undertake such an enterprise.[5] In fact what really interested Laugel was to show that Spencer, notwithstanding his positivistic aspirations, was not an extreme materialist. He even made the effort of translating passages from Spencer's *First Principles* in order to prove that Spencer did not deny spiritualism. The only objection Laugel had to Spencer was that his project to connect the natural sciences and the philosophical sciences was premature.[6]

Spencer was not too pleased with Laugel's review, especially the part that presented his philosophy as an improved version of positivism. For him it was a matter of the utmost importance to prove his intellectual independence and negate any influence whatsoever of Comte's philosophy on his own.[7] His response to Laugel's critique came in the form of an article on the classification of the sciences, whose writing Spencer started before Laugel's review appeared, but to which he added a postscript entitled: "Reasons for Dissenting from the Philosophy of M. Comte"[8]. He hoped in this way to clear the matter of his relation to Comte once and for all. It was not exactly the case. But, to Spencer's fortune, and regardless of the points of resemblance between Spencerism and Positivism – which, in reality, are much more significant than Spencer would have liked to admit - the younger generation of French positivists did not see in him a rival at all. On the contrary, they were enthused and inspired by his writings, as attested in the works of two of the most important figures in the field of psychology: Théodule Ribot and Alfred Espinas.

The philosopher Thédolue Ribot (1839-1916) was Spencer's first French translator. Ribot discovered Spencer's *Principles of Psychology* in 1866 and immediately decided to translate it[9]. In a letter to his friend and fellow student from the "École Normale Supérieure", the philosopher Alfred Espinas (1844-1922), he declared that Spencer's essay was: "one of the most original and interesting books I know. It is Psychology studied in a positive manner, that is […] relying on physiology."[10] Ribot invited Espinas to join him and take part in what he considered to be "a great honour" and a "privilege".[11] Unfortunately, when Ribot finished the translation of Spencer's book in July 1868, he was informed by the author of the latter's intention to rewrite the essay for the new English edition. Ribot was not discouraged. Spencer nominated him to be the translator of the second edition and he decided to wait for the new chapters. This is the reason why the French translation of the two volumes of *Principles of Psychology* appeared only in 1874.[12]

In the meantime *First Principles* was translated and published in 1871[13], giving Ribot another opportunity to express his great admiration. In a letter to Espinas he declared: "The great work of Herbert Spencer, his metaphysics, the *First Principles* was published. [...] In my opinion, it is one of the most marvellous books that exist, and you will not be able to read it without enthusiasm. You will find in it the most complete exposition of the theory of evolution (politic or other). [...] You will find it magnificent."[14] Espinas was not the only one who was thrilled by Spencer's *First Principles*. In fact the French translation of the book marks the beginning of a new and intense phase in the diffusion of Spencerism. The wide dispersal was due, in great part, to the editorial activity of Gustave Baillière, who was not only Spencer's chief publisher, but also the owner of important Reviews like the *Revue des cours scientifique*, and the *Revue philosophique*, founded by Ribot in 1876.

From 1871 to 1881, the high period in the diffusion of Spencerism, Spencer was the most popular author in the *Revue scientifique* (surpassing by far the prominent French writers of the epoch), and more than twenty articles were published under his name in the *Revue philosophique*. They were, for the most part, chapters from books to be published by the Baillière, like *The Study of Sociology*[15], but also commentaries and résumés of Spencer's ideas. Given this parallel diffusion, Spencer was at the time not only the most published foreign thinker in France but also the most reviewed author. He had become the new apostle of the scientific approach to the study of the social sciences, and some of his books, like *First Principles* and *Principles of Sociology* had such great success that they approached the tenth edition towards the end of the century. This feat was so remarkable that the author of a commemorative article published a few months after Spencer's death declared that Spencer's success was much greater in France than in his native Britain[16], thus revealing the degree to which he was omnipresent in the French intellectual milieu.

In Italy as well it seemed as though Spencer's ideas quickly became an integral part of the intellectual scenery. The first references to his writings appeared a decade later than in France, in 1875, in the form of two book reviews: Terenzio Mamiani's review of the French translation of *Principles of Psychology*[17], and Antonio Salandra's review of the original English version of *The Study of Sociology*[18]. It would be a mistake though to assume that, in the Italian context, Spencer's ideas were a novelty of the mid 1870s. According to Salandra's words, "any book written by Herbert Spencer requires no recommendation to those interested in the philosophical and moral disciplines".[19] Salandra was not the only one to think so. In an article from 1904 entitled "Spencer's success in Italy"[20] the philosopher Cesare Ranzoli also affirmed: "Spencer's doctrines found in Italy an intellectual atmosphere already prepared for their reception. Thus, as soon as they became known, they were quickly and widely diffused." In fact, wrote Ranzoli, the similarity between Spencer's ideas and the works of Italian positivists was so striking that one could easily be led to take him for an Italian philosopher.[21]

It is interesting to note that in Italy, as in France, we find amongst the first published references to Spencer that of a non-positivist philosopher, the aforementioned Terenzio Mamiani. Mamiani's contribution in the field of philosophical studies was mainly felt through the journal he founded in 1870, *La Filosofia delle Scuole italiane.* It was the organ of the "Society for the promotion of philosophical and literary studies", founded a year earlier. Mamiani's journal intended to favour the exchange of ideas between diverse philosophical tendencies, the "Italian Schools", as the title had it. In practice, however, Mamiani, who was director of the journal until his death in 1885, used it for the unique purpose of diffusion and defence of his own Platonist philosophy. In his review of Spencer's *Principles of Psychology* he attacked Spencer's "coarse and incoherent" empiricism and concluded that Spencer's psychology was "the least positive that exists".[22]

The same kind of criticism was repeated two years later when Mamiani reviewed the first volume of the French translation of *Principles of Biology*[23]. Neither of these writings was ever translated in whole into Italian. But, in the Italian context of predominance of philosophy over natural sciences, this was by no means a bad omen. Whilst, in France, Spencer's wide-spread diffusion in the 1870's was due in great part to the enthusiasm of the young advocates of psychology, the relative disregard for the scientific parts of Spencer's *System of Synthetic Philosophy* did not prevent the Italian intellectuals from taking an interest in his social theories. On the contrary, the *Study of Sociology* and *Principles of Sociology* have had two different translations[24].

This evaluation is corroborated by recent studies on the diffusion of Darwinism in Italy[25]. These studies have shown that the debate over the theory of evolution, even in its earliest phases, concerned mainly social, political, philosophical and theological issues that transcended Darwin's theory. Philosophical journals eagerly used the new theory in order to revive favourite themes such as: the meaning of history, the existence of progress, and moral dilemmas concerning man and society. One of these journals was the prestigious positivistic *Rivista di Filosofia Scientifica*, which became an important medium for the diffusion of Spencerism.

As indicated by its title – and as is explicitly declared by its founder, the psychiatrist Enrico Morselli, in his introductory article[26] – the *Rivista*'s objective was to show that philosophy and science did not represent two distinct fields of study with opposite methods of investigation. Instead, they were, as Spencer postulated, two aspects of the same unifying principle. That principle, the law of evolution, was to account for all phenomena through the application of two scientific factors: causality and progress. The unity of knowledge corresponded, therefore, to the unity of Nature. Given this brief summary of the *Rivista*'s credo, it is not surprising to see why Spencer was the most important point of reference for diverse authors, Italians and non-Italians.[27]

The *Rivista di Filosofia Scientifica* existed for only a decade – from 1881 to 1891 – a period that can be defined as the "golden age" of Italian positivism. To a certain extent, therefore, the ten year gap that was opened between the first written references to Spencer in

France and in Italy was maintained with regards to the high points in the process of diffusion of his ideas. However, the relatively quick dispersal in Italy resulted in their incorporation into socio-ethical doctrines more or less at the same time as in France. These doctrines turned out to be quite different from Spencer's ideology of *laissez-faire* individualism. In order to understand how this shift came about, it would be helpful to examine the historical circumstances in the time of the creation of the French *Revue scientifique* and the Italian *Rivista di Filosofia Scientifica*, and their political aims.

II

The *Revue des cours scientifiques* was founded in 1864, during a period of relative relaxation in the control put on the press and the educational system by Napoleon the Third. He hoped in this way to appease the rebelling intellectuals who had not pardoned him for the *coup d'Etat* of 1851 – which ended the short-lived Second Republic – or for his alliance with the Church. To Napoleon's dismay, the result of his efforts was an even stronger reaction against the Empire and its clerical ally. The *Revue des cours sceintifiques*, as indicated by its name, was at first destined to publish university lectures given at the Sorbonne and other Parisian "Grandes Ecoles", as well as in foreign establishments, thus making them known to a wider public. Its objective, however, transcended the mere scientific or literary education of the people.

In those days, the liberty to write was still extremely limited in France and so political manifestations often took the form of oratorical addresses. The *Revue scientifique* was therefore, implicitly, a means for the development of free thought and intellectual stimulation. In other words, it was an instrument for political change. Emile Alglave, the director of the *Revue scientifique* and Ribot, his associate and director of the *Revue philosophique*, were aware of the power in their hands. With Baillière's blessing, they used their journals as tribunes for attacks against spiritualism and Catholic Dogma, and they harnessed evolutionism, mainly in its Spencerian version, to promote the Republican cause.

The connection between Spencer's philosophy and the Republican movement is even more clearly manifest in the periodical parallel between the intensive diffusion of Spencerism in the 1870s, and a political event of cardinal importance: the birth of the Third Republic. It was a time of crisis for France. On the one hand, the nation was still shaken by the traumatic experience of the "Comune de Paris" and the upheavals of the Franco-Prussian war. On the other, the pressures of the "social question" were increasingly felt. In order to establish the fragile new regime the republicans sought ideologies that could espouse their ideals and reassure the masses. Spencer, the declared champion of the new sciences, psychology and sociology, and the hero of left wing intellectuals such as Ribot, Espinas, Alglave and Baillière, became the source for such ideologies. It was Science against Religion, Reason against Spiritualism. But the kind of "Science" and "Reason" able to offer an optimistic view of the future and guarantee the reign of order and prosperity.

Alfred Espinas, for example, wrote in his doctoral dissertation on the comparative psychology of animal societies – published in 1877[28] – that the laws of social life and the laws of biological organisation were essentially the same; yet, he hastened to assert that the political and moral implications of this finding need not be feared. On the contrary, nature's behaviour reaffirmed the ethical code, since: "the struggle for existence [...] is not at all the characteristic trait of life, whether in a living body or in a society; it is the coalition for mutual aid in the struggle, it is the respect of the individual, which are life's first condition and most dominant quality".[29] This idea was at the basis of what would become, in the 1890's, the official ideology of the Third Republic, known as "Solidarisme".

The most important exponent of "Solidarisme" was Léon Bourgeois (1851-1925). A jurist by training and member of the Freemasons, Bourgeois occupied practically every official post of importance in the Third Republic. He was, notably, Prime Minister of the first solely Radical cabinet (from November 1st 1895 to April 21st 1896). It was during this time that Bourgeois wrote his famous treatise on Solidarity. It appeared first in 1895 in the journal *La*

Nouvelle Revue as four *Lettres sur le Mouvement social* with the subtitle "The doctrine of solidarity". It was published again in 1896 as a unique brochure[30], rapidly attaining widespread notoriety in French intellectual and political circles.

Léon Bourgeois (1851-1925)

Bourgeois never intended to present his doctrine as an original idea. He was well aware of the affinities between the term of "solidarity" and the revolutionary keyword "fraternity". In fact, he deliberately sought to present "Solidarisme" as the convergence point of different philosophical schools. Solidarity was a more "wholesome" and "profound" concept than its forerunners, because it was a synthesis or, in Bourgeois' words, a "superior agreement between ideas" rather than an "intermediate accord between men". Thanks to the evolution of social thought, at long last the "scientific method" and the "moral idea" could be combined together to form a new doctrine. A doctrine conceived "from a higher point of view" and therefore "able to illuminate a bigger territory in a more even way."[31]

The underlying principle of Bourgeois' theory was that social laws were the manifestation, at a higher level, of the physical, biological and psychological laws that directed the development of all living beings. The most important among them was the "law of association". In its basic definition, it was described as the synergy of individual actions in the common or "solidaire" action.[32] In reality, Bourgeois believed that the whole of biology was summarised in the law of association. He quoted on the matter the economist Charles Gide, another important theoretician of "Solidarisme", who claimed that solidarity was what characterised life: "If we want to define a living being we can only do so by pointing out to the solidarity of functions that links its different parts together – and death is but the rupture of this link…"[33].

Given the identity between the idea of life and the idea of association, Bourgeois deduced that solidarity was also the main feature of evolution. As Spencer showed, biological evolution was the passage from homogeneity to heterogeneity, followed by the differentiation of parts with respect to their function. The most elevated beings were those in which the differentiation of parts was more important and therefore their interdependence bigger. Bourgeois interpreted this as proof to his claim that without solidarity there could be no evolutionary progress, since association was the "condition of success in the struggle for existence".[34] What was true of living organisms was true of the social organism, where:

> …the conflict of forces, the brutal struggle for existence is the departure point, and it is through the evolution of groups […] towards a higher state of intelligence and morality, that the idea of voluntary association emerges and is crystallised, co-ordinating the hostile forces and converting them into useful elements for each individual and the group as a whole; through this slow development of association the terrain is prepared for the substitution of the sate of war and authority by a pacific contractual regime.[35]

Bourgeois' description recalls Spencer's theory on the passage from the military to the industrial society as the additional phase in the evolution of the super-organism. Although Bourgeois did not mention Spencer by name in his book, he quoted the works of French zoologist Edmond Perrier on animal colonies and biological association[36], which were essentially an elaboration of Espinas' thesis from 1877. What is interesting is that, unlike Spencer, for Bourgeois the "development of voluntary association" did not achieve fulfilment in *laissez-faire* individualism, but in the establishment of a political regime based on a special kind of social contract – the "quasi-social contract".

The "quasi-social contract" was a sort of middle way solution between scientific evolutionism and French enlightenment philosophy, especially that of Rousseau, with its ideal of political justice. Man, claimed Bourgeois, cannot exist alone. Because of the evolutionary law of association he depends on the other members of society. The ethical code of mutual aid is, therefore, something that the different members of a given society would have regarded as preconditions of a social contract, if, historically, they had been able to make one.[37] The "quasi-social contract" derived its name from this unique combination: it was partly deterministic, because retroactively inferred as the necessary state of affairs, and partly voluntary, because tacitly approved.

If that is so, then each member of society had natural and moral obligations towards the others. This "social debt", as Bourgeois referred to it, was "a sufficient motive" for social sanctions[38]. In other words, solidarity was the basis of justice and State intervention was the practical programme for achieving the ideal of social justice. Consequently, State intervention was not only legitimate, but necessary. It was needed to guarantee the free exercising of individual liberties and vouch for individual rights, like the right to property, without which economic progress and prosperity were impossible. But, it was also needed in order to establish equality and social security, and make sure that in the struggle for existence the strong do not get stronger at the expense of the weak.

From a political point of view, "Solidarisme" seemed like the perfect compromise between Spencer's extreme liberalism and the dreaded revolutionary socialism. It offered a way to counter the growing problems of the industrial age like poverty, illness, unemployment and social uprising that *laissez-faire* was clearly unable to solve. At the same time, it acted as a panacea against class struggle. This is why Bourgeois' doctrine was so appealing to the Radicals. It was the theoretical justification they sought for their vision of a democratic and just regime based on the principles of 1789 that would later be known as the "Welfare State". It was also a scientific way to fill the vacuum left by the retreat of clericalism while maintaining the ideals of social cohesion and a high ethical code.

By the time of the foundation of the Radical and Radical-Socialist party in 1901, the solidarist credo became the official doctrine of the Third Republic. But around the same time Bourgeois published an article entitled "Solidarisme and its Social consequences", in which he underplayed the role of biological solidarity and stressed the importance of "conscience", or the "moral factor", in directing the evolution of society towards the ideal of justice for all. Bourgeois claimed that while in biological organisms nature acted alone and no one could interfere with her doings, in human societies evolution worked in a different way, because human societies were not simple biological organisms.[39] Spencer, who was this time mentioned by name[40], was called upon as scientific support for this "cardinal" difference between the natural and the social organism.

The problem with natural solidarity was that at times it produced effects of inequality: some profited from it while others didn't. Nature was not unjust, it was simply "a-just".[41] Society, however, was an organism based on contract, and as such its different members needed to give their consent to becoming part of it, if only in a hypothetical way. In other words, society was based on justice, for, logically, no one would give his consent to an unfair arrangement. The introduction of the "moral factor" enabled Bourgeois not only to reaffirm the ideal of social justice, but also to reiterate the necessity of State intervention as a means for mending the unwelcome effects of biological solidarity. It did not escape though the more astute critics who claimed that his "Solidarisme" became, in reality, the doctrine of natural "désolidarisation"[42].

The connection between evolution and politics was not, so it seemed, automatic or simple to prove.   In fact, Spencer's organicism could be interpreted in other ways, as is shown in the following study of the Italian scene and the connection between Spencerism, positivism and socialism.

III

Again, I propose to begin with a closer look at the political aims of the Italian *Rivista di Filosofia Scientifica*.   Officially the *Rivista di Filosofia Scientifica* was not the organ of any specific political movement, but in reality it was clear that the journal meant to be much more than a science popularising periodical.   It aspired to be a vehicle for the remodelling of social sciences on the basis of evolutionary biology, and that meant open battle with the Catholic Church and its Dogma.   In 1881, the year of the foundation of the *Rivista,* Rome had been Italy's capital for only a decade and the Pope still retained considerable power.   The younger generations of Republicans saw in positivism aligned with Spencer's philosophy, powerful weapons against clericalism.   They considered themselves the champions of Civilisation and defenders of rationalism, and hoped to witness the birth of a truly democratic regime.   But the so called "Parliamentary Revolution" of 1876, which finally brought the Left to power after fifteen years of uninterrupted right wing hegemony (basically since the unification of Italy in 1861), left them disillusioned.   From fear of an uncontrollable reinforcement of the extreme Left, Depretis, who was then Prime Minister, decided to sign an agreement with the leader of the opposition that eventually led to a general shifting of the government to the Right.

The dissatisfaction of the young republicans was reinforced by the economic crisis at the beginning of the 1880s and drove them to look for alternatives to the old ideologies of the so-called "Historical Left" – alternatives, which would comply both with their scientific exigencies and their democratic aspirations. Spencer's theory seemed to provide a satisfactory response. Indeed, among the Italian authors of the *Rivista* we frequently find the names of well-known "socialisti della cattedra" (which translates literally to: "socialists of the chair", that is "socialists who are university professors") like: Enrico Ferri, Achille Loria, Giuseppe Sergi, Icilo Vanni, Ugo Rabbeno, Napoleone Colajanni and the famous Cesare Lombroso.

It is no mere coincidence therefore that in the exact same year that the *Rivista di Filosofia Scientifica* ceased to be published, the periodical *Cuore e critica* ["Heart and Critique"] was founded by the Italian socialist Filippo Turati. It was supposed to pick up where the *Rivista* had left off. The change in the name of this periodical that took place two years later, and under which it became famous, reveals its positivistic and political aspirations: *Critica sociale: rivista quindicinale del socialismo scientifico* ["Social Critique: Biweekly Review of Scientific Socialism"]. The most emblematic representative of "Scientific Socialism" was Enrico Ferri (1856-1929), one of Italy's leading political figures at the time.

Ferri started his career as a professor of criminal law, but it was his law practicing activity as the defence for Mantua's farmers after the Venice upheavals of 1886 that won him a reputation as a "socialist" and eventually enabled his election to Parliament. In his inaugural speech Ferri described himself as an "evolutionary sociologist". "Sociologist", because as a scientist and a politician, he was interested in the study of society, which he defined as a natural organism with its own laws of natural development. "Evolutionary", because he believed that the law of gradual evolution dictated the political order just as it dictated the scientific order. He aspired to epitomise a perfect symbiosis between science and politics and proclaimed in his speech, that he did not intend to make any distinction whatsoever between his occupations as a scientist and as a politician[43]. Progress, an unlimited, inexorable, gradual progress was what Ferri saw in nature, and consequently he assigned the legislator the task of favouring progress in what he called the "struggle for good", i.e. the union of all social classes for the constitution of a real democracy.[44]   These declarations were the echoes of the theory he published in an essay on *Socialismo e criminalità* ["Socialism and Criminality"], three years earlier.[45]

Ferri's speech came somewhat as a disappointment to those who expected him to take a clear stand as a "socialist" and adhere to the

Marxian model of class struggle. Unwilling to do so Ferri could not, on the other hand, find a political faction within Parliament which shared his opinions that social problems should be the first on the political agenda, and that they should be dealt with by means of gradual reform.[46] He hoped to witness the birth of a new "really positivist" radical party, and in the meantime, preferred to remain isolated. But in 1893, the year of the creation of the Italian Socialist Party [PSI], Ferri officially announced his adherence to it, thus adhering also to the method of class struggle. A year later he published a book entitled *Socialismo e scienza positiva: Darwin-Spencer-Marx* ["*Socialism and positive science*"], translated into English in 1900[47], in which he purported to explain the motives of his political choice and lay out his ideological tenets.

> A convinced follower of Darwin and Spencer, I propose to demonstrate that Marxian socialism – the only kind that has a positive power and scientific worth, and that had power henceforward to inspire and group the social democrats of the whole civilised world – is the only practical and fruitful complement in social life of that modern scientific revolution, which, inaugurated several centuries back by the revival of the experimental method in all branches of human knowledge, has triumphed in our days thanks to the labours of Charles Darwin and Herbert Spencer. It is true that Darwin, and especially Spencer, stopped short half-way from the final conclusions of religious, political and social order, which necessarily follow from their indisputable premises. But that is only an individual episode, which cannot stop the fulfilment of its practical consequences which accord admirably with the saddest necessities of contemporary life. This is but one more obligation to us to render justice to the scientific and political life of Karl Marx who completes the renovation of modern scientific thought.[48]

Put in simple terms, Ferri's theory was that socialism derived, as a natural consequence, from Darwinism and Spencerian evolutionism. He maintained that the struggle for existence was the basic law in both nature and society, but argued that in social evolution, the aggressive element of the struggle is progressively attenuated and the law of solidarity and co-operation becomes the more efficacious and determinant factor. In other words, with the varying of contents and ideals, the struggle for existence varies in its methods: from violent and physical it gradually becomes pacific and intellectual. Marx clearly understood this, because he made solidarity the essential element in his social theory. Ferri thought that there lay the ultimate proof that Marxist socialism was the logical application and inevitable consequence of evolutionary theory. His short schematic description of the history of the Western world summarised this view: "In primitive humanity the struggle for existence was the same as in the animal world; in the Greek-Latin civilisation the struggle was for civil equality (i.e. the abolition of slavery); during the Middle Ages the struggle was for religious equality, in the end of the eighteenth century the struggle was for political equality, and in the nineteenth century the struggle is for economical equality".[49]

By "equality" Ferri did not intend that all men are equal in an absolute way, nor that the struggle will cease with the advent of socialism. In his eyes, an individual or a society that has no ideal to fight for was as good as dead. In socialism, there were also "survivors" and "defeated" in the struggle for existence. The difference resided in the fact that socialism, and socialism alone, could guarantee that the "fittest" will also be the best. In fact, in a corrupt environment, argued Ferri, the "winners" in the struggle for existence could hypothetically be the wicked or morally weak. Only when the life of everyone is secured, when all get equal conditions of human existence, could there be a fair battle and the truly worthy would prevail. Although Ferri firmly believed that the humanitarian faith in socialism would eventually replace the old religions, he insisted that his theory had nothing utopian about it. Ferri was persuaded that what he did was simply to show – "with mathematical precision" – the direct influence of positive modern science on political thought. The repulsion and even fear that many felt vis-à-vis socialism was not, he argued, a real logical obstacle to this view. On the contrary, it was but another proof of

Spencer's law of evolution-dissolution. In other words, a process of dissolution accompanies every process of evolution and every accomplished progress is perceived as an obstacle to progresses to come.[50]

In a typical manoeuvre, Ferri used his rhetorical talent in order to maintain "scientific socialism" as neutral as possible. He offered his followers a utopian vision of socialism as "the unique force that can give humanity hope of a better future", yet insisted that it was a purely scientific portrayal of reality. He was also careful of stressing too strongly his affiliation with hard line Marxists. As was expected of him, Ferri declared that the struggle for existence was transformed in society to class struggle, yet he warned against all types of revolutionary solutions and hoped that "evolution will be pacifically accomplished without shedding one drop of blood."[51] A society, insisted Ferri, was a natural living organism and therefore could not undergo drastic and artificial changes. To think that one could change society with the use of violence and force would be as senseless as assuming that a young boy can accomplish in a day the physical transformation from childhood to adulthood. Ferri blamed mainly the education system, with its emphasis on the study of Greek and Latin rather than the Natural Sciences, for the "romantic ideals of anarchists and individualists."[52]

Spencer himself turned out to be one of those "romantic idealists". Although he was the "truly great thinker" of evolutionary theory – because the first to import it to the social domain and give it scientific proofs in every branch of human knowledge – his political doctrines represented an arrest in the development of scientific thought. His exacerbated individualism brought him to the point of defending a sort of theoretic absolute anarchism and ignored the evolutionary fact of the continuous progressive prevalence of the species' interests over those of the individual.[53] Consciously or unconsciously, Spencer and many other thinkers refused to recognise the logical consequences of the scientific revolution in the social domain, and continued to hold erroneous political theories simply because they aligned with their personal tendencies [54]

Spencer, when informed that the Italian socialist Ferri had adduced his authority in support of socialism, wrote an indignant protest, which was published in the journal La Riforma in June 1895. In a letter to the editor, Ferri responded that Spencer was under a misapprehension. "No socialist", he wrote, "has ever dreamt to include among the supporters of Socialism the greatest living philosopher [...] whom all the world know to be an extreme individualist. [...] But the personal opinions of Herbert Spencer are a different matter from the logical consequences of the scientific theories on universal evolution, which he has developed farther and better than any other writer, but of which he has not the monopoly nor the power to prohibit their free expansion by the labour of other thinkers."[55]

The "logical consequences of the scientific theories on universal evolution" to which Ferri alluded were rather complex, especially given his own ambiguous position. He started as an adept of gradual reform, then became the champion of revolution and, finally, after many more oscillations, ended as a supporter of Mussolini's Fascism, arguing that Fascism was the expression of a political and economic renaissance, a natural outcome of socialism and part of a larger movement: from individualism to socialism to fascism. In short, fascism was "the affirmation of the supremacy of the State over liberal and libertarian individualism", and represented "an integral and systematic solution to class struggle".[56]

Ferri's interpretation of Spencerian evolutionism as the basis of scientific socialism, and later of fascism, is perhaps the most interesting example of the still unknown process of appropriation of Spencer's ideas by Italian thinkers. Alongside Bourgeois' doctrine of Solidarisme, it testifies to the importance of the context in the interpretation of scientific theories and supports the hypothesis that these theories are not neutral and can be read in many different ways according to the needs of the moment. Thus, while in Britain Spencer's theory was perceived mainly as support for Right-wing conservative ideologies, on the continent, the complex dialectic between themes such as "the struggle for existence" versus "class struggle", or "evolution" versus "revolution" resulted in an unexpected shift. In France and Italy, evolution became the basis for left-wing ideologies, thus investing the scientific model of human development with a different meaning than the one intended by its author.

Bibliography

Becquemont, Daniel, and Mucchielli, Laurent. 1998. *Le cas Spencer*. Paris: PUF.

Boulen, Alfred-Geroges. 1912. *Les idées solidaristes de Proudhon*. Paris: Marchal & Godde.

Bourgeois, Léon. 1896. *La solidarité*. Paris: Armand Colin.

Bourgeois, Léon. 1901. « Solidarisme et ses conséquences sociales ». *Essai d'une philosophie de la solidarité*. Paris : Félix Alcan.

Continenza, Barbara. 1989. "Il dabttito sul darwinismo in Italia nell'Ottocento", *La storia delle scienze*, vol. II. Roma: Bramante.

Corsi, Pietro. 1985. "Recent Studies on Italian Reactions to Darwin", *The Darwinian Heritage*. Princeton University Press.

Duncan, David. 1908. *Life & Letters of Herbert Spencer*. New York: D. Appleton & Co.

Espinas, Alfred. 1877. *Des Sociétés animales : étude d'une psychologie comparée*. Paris : Baillière.

Espinas, Alfred. 1878. *Des Sociétés animales : étude d'une psychologie comparée*. Paris : Baillière.

Ferri, Enrico. 1883. *Socialismo e Criminalità*. Torino: Bocca.

Ferri, Enrico. 1886. "Discorso." *La Nuova Mantova*, 20 maggio.

Ferri, Enrico. 1894. *Socialismo e scienza positiva*. Roma: Casa editrice italiana.

Ferri, Enrico. 1900. *Socialism and Positive Science*. Translated by Robert Rives La Monte, New York: New York International Library Publishing Co.

Ferri, Enrico. 1903. *Autobiografia*. Milano: Leone Magnaghi.

Ferri, Enrico. 1905. *Socialism and Positive Science*. Translated from the French edition of 1896 by Edith C. Harvey. London: Independent Labour Party.

Ferri, Enrico. 1927. *Il fascismo in Italia e l'opera di B. Mussolini*. Mantova: Paladino.

Hayward, J.E.S. 1959. "Solidarity: the Social History of an Idea in the Nineteenth Century". *International Review of Social History*, 4: 261-284.

Hayward, J.E.S. 1961. "The Official Social Philosophy of the French Third Republic: Léon Bourgeois and Solidarism". *International Review of Social History*, 6: 19-48.

Landucci, Giovanni. 1977. *Darwinismo a Firenze. Tra scienza e ideologia (1860-1900)*. Firenze: Leo S. Olschki.

Laugel, Auguste.1864. "Les etudes philosphiques en Angleterre, M. Herbert Spencer". *Revue des Deux Mondes* 49 : 930-956

Littré, Emile. 1863. *Auguste Comte et la philosophie positive,* Paris: Hachette.

Mamiani, Terenzio. 1875. "Recensione di Herbert Spencer : *Principes de Psychologie.*" *La Filosofia delle Scuole Italiane*, 11: 123-133.

Mamiani, Terenzio. 1877. "Recensione di Herbert Spencer: *Principes de Biologie.*" , vol. I, Paris, 1877, *Filosofia delle Scuole italiane* 15: 421-428.

Morselli, Enrico. 1881. "La Filosofia e la Scienza." *Rivista di Filosofia Scientifica.* 1: I-VIII

Pancaldi, Giuliano. 1977. *Charles Darwin : "storia" ed "economia" della natura.* Firenze: La Nuova Italia.

Rageot, Gaston. 1904. "Herbert Spencer et la philosophie de la vie". *Revue des Deux mondes* 22 : 808-843.

Ranzoli, Cesare. 1904. "La fortuna di Erberto Spencer in Italia." *Rivista di filosofia e scienze affini*, 1: 217-236, 440-467.

Ribot, Théodule. 1957. « Lettres de Théodule Ribot à Alfred Espinas ». *Revue philosophique*: 1-14.

Rossi, Lino. 1988. *Dalla filosofia alle scienze dell'uomo: Riviste scientifiche e origine delle scienze sociali in Italia (1871-1891).* Milano: Franco Angeli.

Salandra, Antonio. 1875. "Recensione di H. Spencer: *The Study of Sociology* (London 1874)." *Giornale napoletano di Filosofia e Lettere.* 1: 169-172

Spencer, Herbert. 1864. *The Classification of the Sciences: To Which Are Added Reasons for Dissenting from the Philosophy of M. Comte.* London: Williams & Norgate.

Spencer, Herbert. 1871. *Les premiers principes.* Paris: Germer Bailiière.

Spencer, Herbert. 1873. *The Study of Sociology.* Paris: Germer Baillière.

Spencer, Herbert. 1874. *Principes de psychologie.* Paris: Germer Baillière.

Spencer, Herbert. 1881. *Introduzione allo studio della sociologia.* Translated by Sofia Fortini Santarelli. Milano: Fratelli Dumolard.

Spencer, Herbert. 1881-1889. *Principi di sociologia.* Translated by Antonio Salandra e Guglielmo Salvadori. Torino: Unione Tipografica Editrice Torinese.

Spencer, Herbert. 1904[1]. *Herbert Spencer: An Autobiography.* Vol. I-II. New-York: D. Appleton.

Spencer, Herbert. 1904[2]. *Introduzione alla scienza sociale.* Torino: Bocca.

Spencer, Herbert. 1922. *Principi di sociologia*. Translated by G. Egidi. Padova: Rinfreschi.

Notes and References

*   This article is part of a PhD dissertation on "Late Nineteenth Century Spencerism : Evolutionism and Political Doctrines in Italy & France (1870-1914) - A Comparative Study"

1   Becquemont, Mucchielli, 1998, p. 218.

2   Littré, 1863.

3   Laugel, 1864.

4   *Ibid.* p. 934.

5   *Ibid.* p. 935.

6   *Ibid.* pp. 954-957.

7   Spencer, 1904[1], vol. II, p. 127

8   Spencer, 1864.

9   Ribot, 1957, p. 2.

10   *Ibid.*

11   *Ibid.*, p. 4.

12   Spencer, 1874.

13   Spencer, 1871.

14   Ribot, 1957, p. 7.

15   Spencer, 1873.

16   Rageot, 1904, 808.

17   Mamiani, 1875, pp. 123-133.

18   Salandra, 1875, pp. 169-172.

19   *Ibid.* p. 169

20   Ranzoli, 1904. pp. 217-236; 440-467.

21   *Ibid.* pp. 227-229.

22   Mamiani, 1875, pp. 128, 133.

23   Mamiani, 1877.

24   See list of references at the end of this article.

25   Corsi, 1985, pp. 711-729; Pancaldi, 1977, pp. 161-206; Landucci, 1977: Continenza, 1989.

26   Morselli, 1881, pp. I-VIII.

[27] For a list of the articles published during the decade of existence of the *Rivista di Filosofia Scientifica* see Rossi, 1988, pp. 211-244.

[28] Espinas, 1877.

[29] Espinas, 1878, pp. 128, 152-153.

[30] Bourgeois, 1896.

[31] *Ibid.* pp. 6-7, 12, 16.

[32] *Ibid.* pp. 27, 58.

[33] Bourgeois, 1901, p. 3.

[34] *Ibid.* p. 3.

[35] Bourgeois, 1896, pp. 96-97.

[36] *Ibid.* pp. 59-60; Bourgeois, 1901, p. 4.

[37] *Ibid.* pp. 132, 136-137.

[38] *Ibid.* p. 116.

[39] Bourgeois, 1901, p. 7.

[40] *Ibid.*

[41] *Ibid.* pp. 9-10.

[42] Boulen, 1912, p. 20.

[43] Ferri, 1886.

[44] *Ibid.*

[45] Ferri, 1883.

[46] Ferri, 1903, p. 9.

[47] Ferri, 1894, 1900, 1905.

[48] Ferri, 1905, p. XI.

[49] Ferri, 1894, pp. 37-39; 46-47, 71, 90.

[50] *Ibid.* pp. 33, 54, 56, 113, 127.

[51] *Ibid.* pp. 148, 156, 168.

[52] *Ibid.* pp. 136-137.

[53] *Ibid.* p. 127. Ferri attributed to old age Spencer's "politicalaberrations". *Justice* and *Positive and Negative Beneficence* were, he declared, the fruits of a senile mind. *Ibid.* p. 102.

[54] *Ibid.* pp. 92, 154.

[55] *Ibid.* p. 153.

[56] Ferri, 1927, pp. 85-87.

4. Herbert Spencer's Influence on Economics

John Laurent

Herbert Spencer is widely regarded as a major figure in, indeed a founder of, sociology, as in his books *Principles of Sociology* and *The Study of Sociology*, but he is less known today as an influential figure in economics. And in so far as formal theorising goes, it is true that Spencer didn't write extensively on this subject: the word "economics", at any rate, does not appear in the title of any of his published works, so far as I am aware. Yet it is also recognised that certain major economists, notably Alfred Marshall (1842–1924) in the UK, and the American John Bates Clark (1847–1938), acknowledged a deep intellectual debt to Spencer, and according to Geoff Hodgson, Professor of Economics at the University of Hertfordshire, given the importance of Marshall and Clark, it could almost be said that Spencer was a "grandfather" of modern economics.[1] Certainly Spencer's influence is palpable in Clark's (1894) *The Philosophy of Wealth*, for instance, such as where Clark writes that "It is a discovery of recent times that a society is not merely like an organism, but … is one in literal fact,"[2] and Marshall, citing Spencer, refers to "the biological view"[3] of economics which seeks to take into account the "living and ever-changing economic organism".[4] Marshall's most famous student, John Maynard Keynes, for a time anyway, used the same language. But I will return to this theme of the influence on economic theory of Spencer's organic metaphor later; first, I want to look at Spencer's influence on economics in a more restricted sense – that on economic policy, specifically, land policy.

Michael Shermer's recent biography of A.R. Wallace – *In Darwin's Shadow* – has numerous references to Spencer, including a number in a ten-page discussion of Wallace's socialism and his debt to Spencer in this connection. Spencer and socialism? Surely these terms can only be used in antithesis? – yet, Shermer, writes: "If [Robert] Owen planted the socialist seed in Wallace, the noted evolutionist and polymathic synthesist Herbert Spencer nurtured it into full developnent".[5] What Shermer is referring to are Spencer's early views on land nationalisation, first published in 1851 in *Social Statics*. An 1868 edition of this book, which I found in the Queensland Parliamentary Library, still contains these views which, under the heading "The Right to the Use of the Earth", read in part as follows:

Briefly reviewing the argument, we see that the right of each man to the use of the earth, limited only by the like rights of his fellow men, is immediately deducible from the law of equal freedom. We see that the maintenance of this right necessarily forbids private property in land. On examination all existing titles to such property turn out to be invalid [Spencer cites "violence, fraud, and the prerogative of force" going back to Norman times in England]; those founded on reclamation inclusive. It appears that not even an equal apportionment of the earth amongst its inhabitants could generate a legitimate proprietorship. We find that if pushed to its ultimate consequences, a claim to exclusive possession of the soil involves a land-owning despotism ... And we find ... that the theory of the co-heirship of all men to the soil, is consistent with the highest civilisation; and that, however difficult it may be to embody that theory in fact, Equity certainly commands it to be done.[6]

As I said, I am quoting an 1868 edition of *Social Statics*, which I located in the Queensland Parliamentary Library. The interesting thing about this copy is that it is not normally accessible to the public, so that there is a good likelihood that any annotations or markings in the book – such as a pencil marking of the passage I have just read – have been made by Queensland parliamentarians. Be this as it may, the library also contains Wallace's *Land Nationalisation: Its Necessity and Its Aims* – the socialistic book in which Wallace acknowledges his debt to Spencer's views – and this also contains marked passages, including a quote from Spencer.[7] But however influential Spencer's arguments for land nationalisation, either directly through *Social Statics* or indirectly through Wallace, may have been on Queensland parliamentarians, it is quite clear that another author whose books are prominent in the Queensland Parliamentary Library – Henry George – was profoundly influential in Queensland, and indeed in all the Australian colonies and later States, and that this influence also owed much to Herbert Spencer. The title page of *A Perplexed Philosopher*, one of George's books in the Queensland Parliamentary Library (the other three books are also in the library – all the books I have referred to were acquired in the 1890s), and as may be seen from the subtitle, this book purports to be "An Examination of Mr. Herbert Spencer's Various Utterances on the Land Question with some Incidental Reference to his Synthetic Philosophy". The whole book is about Spencer, and again, it was apparently well used by Queensland parliamentarians: among the marked passages is, for example, the paragraph from *Social Statics* quoted previously, transcribed in full by George.

Spencer's (and Wallace's) arguments for land *nationalisation* were not, however, quite what Henry George had in mind in his advocacy of access to land ownership expressed in *A Perplexed Philosopher*, as well as in his probably more well known book, *Progress and Poverty*. George's arguments were complex and at times opaque, and were open to different interpretations; but essentially the idea was that a single tax on the unimproved value of land – the "unearned increment" – was all that was needed by governments to raise the funds necessary for "repurchase" (from leasehold) of land for small-holders. The idea caught on in Australia and New Zealand where, notwithstanding indigenous claims (which were for the most part conveniently ignored), governments assumed ownership of all land.[8] Both governments and landless voters saw merit in the concept, and did not need especially strong persuasion from George, either through his books or from the writer himself in a lecture tour of the Antipodes in 1890, in which he drew large crowds in Sydney and rural New South Wales as well as in Brisbane and coastal towns in Queensland, and in which George made reference to Spencer.[9] Following George's tour, Single Tax Leagues were established, the "Manifesto" of the one in New Zealand reading in part as follows:

> [T]his league holds that all unearned increment should be secured to the community, to whose presence and

industry that value is due. It is proposed to assess it by means of a tax on unimproved land value, such tax to be gradually increased, at the same time remitting other taxes which fall at present on labour and capital, beginning with the remission of taxes on the necessities of life, until all taxes are levied on unimproved land values only – [the] "Single Tax".[10]

The Manifesto went on to state that this principle should "be carried to such an extent that mere holding of land without using it will become impossible", and that the proposal "would cheapen land and lighten the burdens of the community generally". The similarity to Spencer's views is obvious. Spencer had argued in *Social Statics* that:

If ... the assumption that land can be held as property involves that the whole globe may become the private domain of a part of its inhabitants; and if, by consequence, the rest of its inhabitants ... can exist ... only by consent of the landowners; it is manifest, that an exclusive possession of the soil necessitates an infringement of the law of equal freedom. For men who cannot "live and move and have their being" without the leave of others cannot be equally free with those others.[11]

Public ownership of land, in Spencer's view, would mean that '[i]nstead of being in the possession of individuals, the country would be held by the great corporate body – Society'.[12]

Whatever the merit of these arguments, they clearly found appeal in "Newest England", the title of a 1902 book about New Zealand by the American writer Henry Demarest Lloyd, who visited the country and "found Henry George everywhere spoken of with the greatest admiration".[13] In Queensland, the canny Liberal Premier (later first Chief Justice of the High Court of Australia), Samuel Griffith, was quick to recognise this appeal, and it is generally agreed that Griffith's Land Act of 1884, under which legislation was enacted authorising the resumption of approximately half the land granted in pastoral leases by the government,[14] was influenced by George's writings (and Griffith had discussions with George when the latter visited Brisbane in

1890[15]). With the election of Queensland's first Labor government in 1915, the Treasurer, E.G. ("Red Ted") Theodore, introduced a Land Tax Bill which, according to Theodore, could be "operated to effect certain reforms – economic reforms – in the affairs of the State in order to protect the interests of the people", since it enabled "the Government to impose a tax on the truest economic basis, upon the unearned increment of land values" and had the advantage of "making land more easily available since it makes it extremely unprofitable for anyone to hold large aggregations of land".[16] In language which would have pleased Spencer, the Bill, Theodore claimed, "would have the effect – the incontestable effect – of destroying, or tending to destruction, of private monopolies in land".[17]

Theodore's Land Tax Bill was rejected by the then Queensland upper house, the Legislative Council, as was a Land Act Amendment Act of 1920, which sought to repeal a pre-Labor piece of legislation which disallowed increasing pastoral rents by more than 50 per cent over the preceding (usually five-year) term, and which were only a third of the rents levied on small-holders.[18] Many pastoral leases were held by banks and overseas speculators, and according to Theodore (now Premier) a "grave injustice" had been done to the community as a result of this prior legislation.[19] The end result of this continued frustration of the Theodore government's legislative program was the abolition of the Legislative Council through a process of stacking the chamber with pro-government "suicide" appointees who voted themselves out of office in an extraordinary series of events in 1922. Queensland remains to this day the only unicameral parliament among the Australian States.[20] With the Council out of the way, Theodore could embark on projects such as the Dawson Valley irrigation scheme, west of Bundaberg, which was commenced in 1923 on the basis of perpetual lease on some 200,000 acres of land resumed from pastoral holdings. A new town, Theodore – "the first model garden city of Australia" – was surveyed on the river flats, and while the project was slow to get going, and struggled through the 1930s Depression years, it eventually proved a success, with cotton and various grains grown on the rich black soil plains of the area.[21]

There is no question that these developments owed much to Henry George, and ultimately to Herbert Spencer's writing in *Social Statics*. Whatever the significance of the marked passages in the books by these authors and A.R. Wallace in the Queensland Parliamentary Library, economists are agreed on the influence of Georgist theories in the Antipodes. According to Colin Clark, "[t]here are no countries in the world in which [George's] ideas have had so much influence as Australia and New Zealand".[22] Clark explained that the first majority Federal Labor government in Australia imposed a land tax on larger properties throughout the country in 1910, and that this was not repealed until 1952. Writing in 1958, Clark went on to point out that, in fact, all Australian municipalities at the time still "derive[d] practically the whole of their revenue from taxes imposed, exactly as Henry George advocated, solely on the unimproved value of the land, exempting buildings and cultivations".[23]

As mentioned, Spencer's and Wallace's land *nationalisation* went further than George – George rejected the description of his ideas as socialist; though in Australia and New Zealand the issue was really somewhat hypothetical inasmuch as, as I said, on colonisation, the government had assumed ownership of all land. Thus when, in Victoria, the followers of Henry George got together and formed a Land *Nationalization* League, joining forces with followers of Wallace's ideas, George was not pleased: "I am not a land nationalisationist, as the English and German and Australian land nationalisationists well know", he wrote in *A Perplexed Philosopher*.[24] And notwithstanding *Spencer's* antipathy to socialism, his ideas on the land question were actually closer to Wallace's than to George's. In 1881 Spencer wrote to Wallace, "I fully sympathize in the general aims of your proposed Land Nationalisation Society" (though he demurred on "a program so definite as that which you send me"), and later the same year he wrote expressing reservation about George's *Progress and Poverty*, observing, at one point: "I do not in the least believe that from the primitive system of communistic ownership to a high and finished system of State ownership, such as we may look for in the future, there could be any transition without passing through such stages as we have seen, and which exist now."[25] One can only speculate on what Spencer might have thought of Theodore's "socialistic" land legislation (as it was described by Opposition members at the time[26]); certainly Spencer's views changed between 1868 and 1892, when a later edition of *Social Statics* was published with *The Man versus The State* in one volume, omitting the "Right to the Use of the Earth" chapter.

George, in *A Perplexed Philosopher*, published the following year, was aware of this, berating Spencer for "having now ... definitely withdrawn" all that he had "originally said about the relation between men and the earth". Nevertheless, George, the non-socialist, tried to understand Spencer's seeming about-face. Referring to the essays making up *The Man versus The State* part of the new book (originally published in the *Contemporary Review* in 1884), George noted that the essays were "strongly individualistic, condemning even bitterly any use of governmental powers or funds to regulate the conditions of labour ...", and that in this Spencer was "continuing and accentuating a line begun in 'Social Statics' and, in the view of those who think as I do, was in the main right; for governmental interferences and regulations and bonuses are in their nature restrictions on freedom, and cannot cure evils that primarily flow from denials of freedom".[27]

Interestingly, the Fabian socialist H.G. Wells, in his later book, *The Work, Wealth and Happiness of Mankind*, was to argue similarly[28]; however, George was not happy with what he saw as clearly a different Spencer in *The Man versus The State*. To illustrate, George quotes a paragraph from Spencer's essay "The Coming Slavery" in this work containing a reference to himself that he (George) vigorously repudiates. The paragraph reads in part as follows:

> Communistic theories, partially indorsed by one Act of Parliament after another ... are being advocated more and more vociferously by popular leaders, and urged on by organized societies. There is movement for land nationalization which, aiming at a system of land-tenure, equitable in the abstract, is, as all the world knows, pressed by Mr. George and his friends with avowed disregard for the just claims of existing owners.[29]

Yet George still hopes that Spencer has not entirely abandoned his earlier position on the land question: something is still salvageable, he believes, in these words from *The Man versus The State*, viz., "the admission that the movement for land nationalization is 'aiming at a system of land-tenure equitable in the abstract.'" Spencer has not "reached the point of utterly denying the truth he had seen", George goes on, "[t]he abolition of private property in land he still admits is equitable in the abstract".[30]

So, notwithstanding an undeniable hardening in Spencer's philosophical position between the *Social Statics* of 1868 and the revised version of 1892 accompanying *The Man versus The State*, Spencer's concern for "equity" – the level playing field version – can be seen as a continuing theme. In earlier writings like "Railway Morals and Railway Policy", from October 1854, Spencer, on the one hand, could refer to "that normal competition which is advantageous to all", while on the other hand could distinguish this from "[t]he ... intense and deleterious ... competition between rival companies in extension and branch making, which has already done vast injury". Spencer notes Robert Stephenson's estimate that of the £250 million already raised for railway construction, fully £70 million had been "needlessly spent in [legal] contests, in duplicate lines, in 'the multiplication of an immense number of schemes prosecuted at an almost reckless expense'." This sum, Spencer approvingly quotes Stephenson as saying, was in fact "a very inadequate representative of the actual loss in point of convenience, economy and other circumstances connected with the traffic which the public has sustained *by reason of parliamentary carelessness in legislating for railways*". Under an "*equitable interpretation of the proprietory contract*", Spencer writes, "the greater part of this expense could have been avoided" (my emphasis).[31]

Spencer, then, sees a role for government in his vision of society. To that extent, critics such as T.H. Huxley may not be quite accurate in their charge that Spencer had too much faith in the spontaneous workings of the social organism, and that *laissez-faire* should be allowed free play without government meddling. Spencer's most complete statement in this connection is his essay "The Social Organism" in the *Westminster Review* of January 1860.

In this essay, Spencer argues that "The whole of our industrial organization, from its most conspicuous features down to its minutest details, has become what it is, not only without legislative guidance, but, to a considerable extent, in spite of legislative hindrances", and he draws analogies from the natural world in support of his case. For example, comparing the "body politic" with primitive and more highly evolved biological organisms, Spencer writes as follows:

> In complexity, our large civilized nations as much exceed the primitive savage ones, as a vertebrate animal does a zoophyte. And while in simple communities, as in simple creatures, the mutual dependence of parts is so slight, that subdivision or mutilation causes but little inconvenience; in complex communities as in complex creatures, you cannot remove or injure any considerable organ without producing great disturbance or death of the rest.[32]

Society then, or perhaps one can say, the economy, in Spencer's view, is a spontaneous natural growth, like any living entity, and must be allowed free rein. Thus, according to Spencer, have the beneficial results of the increasing division of labour become manifest in the Industrial Revolution of Spencer's Britain. T.H. Huxley, however, begged to differ. In "Administrative Nihilism", his response to Spencer's essay, Huxley wrote thus:

> All this appears to be very just. But if the resemblance between the body physiological and the body politic is any indication, not only of what the latter is, and how it has become what it is, but of what it ought to be, and what it is tending to become, I cannot but think that the real force of the analogy is totally *opposed* to the negative view of State function.
>
> Suppose that, in accordance with this view, each muscle were to maintain that the nervous system had no right to interfere with its contraction, except to prevent it from hindering the contraction of another muscle; or each gland, that it had a right to secrete, so long as its secretion interfered with no other; suppose every

separate cell left free to follow its own "interest" and
laissez-faire, lord of all, what would become of the body
physiological?[33]

Huxley was not alone in this view. Late nineteenth and early
twentieth-century socialists, as Michael Taylor (in *Herbert Spencer and
the Limits of the State*) has shown, argued similarly, effectively taking
Spencer's vision of the inexorable process of social evolution and
turning it on its head. Sidney Webb, for example, in a contribution
to Alfred Marshall's *Economic Journal* for June 1891, asserted that it
"is as a State, i.e., as an ordered political society, that a social
organism becomes more distinctly conscious of its existence as an
organism and consequently most capable of regulating [its]
tendencies";[34] and Elsie Mann, wife of the dockers' strike leader
Tom Mann, in the Melbourne *Socialist* of April 1906, claimed that
to "call one's self an evolutionary Socialist … means nothing …
beyond an endorsement of the application of the evolutionary
theory of Socialism, which was admitted by Herbert Spencer, who,
through miscomprehension, hated and abhorred Socialism".[35]

So perhaps a major part of Spencer's influence on economics
was the opposite of what he intended? To some extent, yes:
however, the picture is a little more complicated. As we have seen,
Henry George, for one, was entirely in accord with Spencer on
"governmental interferences and regulations" which were "in their
nature restrictions on freedom". And in *Progress and Poverty*, George
argues his case by citing Spencer's argument as I quoted him
earlier. In George's words: "The lower the stage of social
development, the more society resembles one of those lowest of
animal organisms, which are without organs or limbs, and from
which a part may be cut and yet live. The higher the stage of social
development, the more society resembles those higher organisms
in which functions and powers are specialized, and each member is
vitally dependent on the others".[36] George, then, is endorsing
Spencer's "self-organisation" thesis, with a minimal role for
governments. John Bates Clark, also no socialist ("The socialistic
state would destroy personal freedom"[37]) uses the same metaphor:

The analogy between society and the human body was
familiar to the ancients. It is a discovery of recent times

that a society is not merely like an organism; it is one in literal fact. It is a late discovery that social organisms develop earliest in forms corresponding, not to man, but to the lowest animals. The same characteristics which rank an animal as high or low in the scale of development give a similar rank to a society. ... The more unlike are the parts in form and function, and the more the structure is subjected to the directing influence of a thinking organ, the higher is the society in the scale of organic development.

Clark concludes: "The solidarity of society is a primary economic fact. Political economy treats, not merely of the wealth of individuals ... but of the wealth of society as an organic unit".[38]

Spencer apparently agreed, at least to judge by pre-1892 editions of *Social Statics*, where he argues that his case for "The Right to the Use of the Earth" was simply "consistent with the highest state of civilization. ... The change required [being] simply ... a change of landlords. Separate ownership would merge into the joint-stock ownership of the public. Instead of being in the possession of individuals, the country would be held by the great corporate body – society".[39] And in Spencer's view (writing in 1871), this need not involve a contradiction with his conception of the role of the state. In answer to Huxley's criticisms, Spencer *agreed*, concerning the "body physiological", that "a form of government, or control, or coordination, develops as fast as these systems of organs develop. ... From instant to instant there must be quick adjustment to occasions that are more or less new; and hence there requires a complex and centralized nervous apparatus, to which all these organs are promptly and completely obedient".[40]

But Spencer draws a distinction between the "outer" and "inner" parts of an individual organism, between the "parts which hold direct converse with the environment" and the parts which are concerned with internal processes. Turning to the social organism, and the "analogies of structure and function which may be traced in it", Spencer again draws this distinction, arguing that a society, like an individual, has on the one hand a set of structures for dealing with external contingencies – armies, navies and so forth, and on the other hand "an industrial organization which carries on all those processes that make possible the national life". It is when these two areas of action become confused, in Spencer's view, when governments take an excessive responsibility for a society's internal functioning, that problems arise. The modes of action of government agencies dealing with external concerns, and those dealing with internal matters, Spencer argues, are necessarily different. As Spencer has it:

> For adjustment to the varying and incalculable changes in the environment, the external organs, offensive and defensive, must be capable of prompt combination; and that their actions may be quickly combined to meet each exigency as it arises, they must be completely subordinated to a supreme executive power – armies and navies must be despotically controlled. Quite otherwise is it with the regulatory apparatus required for the industrial system. This, which carries on the nutrition of a society, as the visceral system carries on the nutrition of an individual, has a regulative in great measure distinct from that which regulates the external organs. It is not by any "order in council" that farmers are determined to grow so much wheat and so much barley, or to divide their land in due proportion between arable and pasture.[41]

One may quibble about the generality of Spencer's distinction – whether or not governments should play any part in national production in times of war, for example – but there is no denying the ingenuity of the analogy. And economists have been following Spencer's lead in using biological analogy in their models of the economy ever since, in Spencer's own time, as already indicated, most saliently in the work of J.B. Clark and Alfred Marshall. But they were not the first to do so. That honour goes, it would seem (at least in terms of book-length writing) to William Edward Hearn, Professor of History and Political Economy at the University of Melbourne from 1855 to 1878. Hearn appears to have been largely forgotten in mainstream economic theory, and even in his own time he attracted little notice outside of Australia. But his methodology, drawing extensively upon biological models, appears prescient, given what currently seems to be a resurgence of interest in such models, in books with titles like *Evolutionary Economics, Evolution and Path Dependence in Economic Ideas, Evolutionary Macroeconomics*, etc. Perhaps there might be some renewed interest in Hearn; but however this might be, there is no question that there has been renewed interest in Marshall of late, and to a lesser extent, in J. B. Clark, and that this in turn has brought Spencer back into focus.

There is acknowledgement of a debt to Hearn's now largely unknown *Plutology* (Melbourne, 1863), with its early demand-side ("wants") economics, in Marshall's (1898) *Principles of Economics* (and there is a copy of the book in Marshall's library[42]); and a cursory glance through the book quickly reveals the importance of Spencer's writings for the author. Spencer's *Essays* are cited extensively, and in Hearn's words,

> The same phenomena which ... characterize the evolution of an individual may be observed in the evolution of society. In the complexity of its social structure, and in the definite character of its several organs, no less than in its actual bulk, the English nation exceeds an aboriginal tribe at least as much as one of the higher mammals exceeds a zoophyte.[43]

Hearn cites numerous examples of this complexity and interdependence, such as in the various tasks involved in the manufacture of woollen goods in the north of England; and this picture was taken up by Alfred Marshall, who wrote in 1898, for example (citing Hearn and Spencer), in a chapter on Industrial Organisation:

> [E]conomists have ... owed much to the many profound analogies which have been discovered between social and especially industrial organization on the one side, and the physical organization of the higher animals on the other. ... [These analogies] have gradually been supplemented by others, and have at last established their claim to illustrate a fundamental unity of action between the laws of nature in the physical and in the moral world. This

> central unity is set forth in the general rule ... that the
> development of the organism, whether social or physical,
> involves an increasing subdivision of functions between
> its separate parts on the one hand, and on the other, a
> more intimate connection between them.[44]

Spencer himself, in *First Principles*, talks about the "advance from the homogeneous to the heterogeneous in the industrial organization of society", when "roads and other means of transit become numerous and good", and "different districts begin to assume different functions and to become mutually dependent". The calico manufacturer, Spencer continues,

> locates himself in this county, the woollen manufacturer
> in that; silks are produced here, lace there; stockings in
> one place, shoes in another; pottery, hardware, cutlery,
> come to have their special towns; and ultimately every
> locality grows more or less distinguished from the rest by
> the leading occupation carried on in it. Nay, more, this
> sub-division of functions shows itself not only among
> the different parts of the same nation, but amongst
> different nations. The exchange of commodities which
> free-trade promises so greatly to increase, will ultimately
> have the effect of specializing, in a greater or less degree,
> the industry of each people.[45]

Apart from predicting the globalisation of present-day economics, the influence of Spencer on Marshall is obvious. This is corroborated by Marshall's own acknowledgement, in Mary Paley Marshall's account of her husband's resting, during hikes in the Swiss Alps, to take "a long pull at some book – Goethe or Hegel or Kant or Herbert Spencer", and by the copies of thirteen of Spencer's works, including *Social Statics* and *First Principles*, in Marshall's library in Cambridge, a number of which have been annotated by Marshall.[46] It is not clear what Marshall thought of Spencer's arguments for land nationalisation, but there is ample evidence of his interest in Henry George's ideas. As Marshall's biographer, Peter Groenewegen explains, George's *Progress and Poverty* had a large sale in Britain in the early 1880s and this secured a ready audience for the author when he visited the country in

1884. Marshall attended at least one lecture by George, and himself lectured on George's theories in extension classes at Bristol University College.[47] As Peter Groenewegen has shown, Marshall was sympathetic with the concept of restricting the rights of private property in land for social reasons, though he could not subscribe to the single tax notion – he doubted whether, for example, "taking taxes off spirits would be an unmixed benefit". But in all, according to Groenewegen, Marshall's lectures reveal a sympathy for socialism of the "small s" variety and a position on land taxation and the unearned increment not dissimilar to George's and Spencer's.[48]

Regarding the organic analogy, it has to be said that Marshall's and Spencer's use of this carries some problems. To begin with, there is the question of the *scale* at which the analogy is supposed to operate. The use of this figure of speech is of course an old one: it goes back at least to Plato, but it is also a very flexible device. Plato himself applied it to the city-state of his time; the Australian travel writer, Peter Pinney, described the Balkans market town of Prizren's "pulsing heart", with its "arteries" of streets leading into the same "swollen with citizens and country folk"; and Paul Theroux spoke of the Marquesan island of Takapotou and its community as "like a small fragile organism".[49] Spencer, as we have seen, could, by inference anyway, apply the metaphor to the world as a whole; Hearn could apply it to "the English nation"[50], and J.M. Keynes could refer to nations as "giant organic units".[51]

The lability of the term "social organism" is thus apparent, and perhaps it is not surprising that while Keynes, in his earlier writings, used it (more than likely borrowing it – and another term, "economic organism" – from his mentor, Marshall[52]), he had abandoned it by the time he wrote his most well-known book, *The General Theory of Employment, Interest and Money*[53]. In *A Treatise on Money* (1930), Keynes also points to another difficulty he has with Spencer's and Marshall's "social organism" idea, and that is with the tension in Marshall's writing between evolutionary *change*, on the one hand, and the functioning of an economy as a system in *equilibrium,* on the other. Keynes writes as follows:

> Marshall's *Principles of Economics* was published forty years
> ago. For thirty years after its publication the progress of
> economic theory was very slight. By 1920 Marshall's
> theory of economic equilibrium had been absorbed but
> not materially improved. Unfortunately Marshall … was
> a little disposed sometimes to camouflage the essentially
> static character of his equilibrium theory with many wise
> and penetrating *obiter dicta* on dynamical problems. …
> But now at last we are, I think, on the eve of a new step
> forward which, if it is made successfully, will enormously
> increase the applicability of theory to practice; namely, an
> advance to an understanding of the detailed behaviour of
> an economic system which is *not* in static equilibrium (my
> emphasis).[54]

Keynes does not use the word "evolution" as such, but it is fairly
clear that something of the kind is what he has in mind when he
talks about "dynamical problems". (In any case, Keynes's deep
interest in evolution is well attested to in other writings, as in
"Economic Possibilities for our Grandchildren", where he says
things like "The economic problem, the struggle for subsistence,
has been … the primary … problem not only of the human race,
but of the whole of the biological kingdom from the beginning of
life in its most primitive forms".[55]) Marshall, indeed, had been
similarly interested in "evolution", as we have seen, but it was by
and large not Darwinian evolution. The evolutionary *change* with
which Marshall was primarily concerned was Spencerian rather
than Darwinian. It is true that Darwin's name appears three times
in the index of *Principles of Economics* (i.e. the fourth, 1898, edition[56]),
but these entries relate to passing references, revealing little real
understanding of Darwin's central ideas, whereas Spencer's name
appears seven times, and for the main part in the context of the
extended discussions I have been quoting.

And these Spencerian discussions in Marshall *themselves* contain
elements of the tension between "evolution" – or, at least, historic
change – and equilibrium, as referred to by Keynes. The title of
one of Spencer's most influential books in this respect is, after all,
Social Statics – as another economist with an interest in evolution,

Thorstein Veblen, pointed out as long ago as 1908; and one of the longest chapters in Spencer's *First Principles* is titled "Equilibration". It contains sentences like, "The internal actions constituting social functions exemplify the general principle. ... Supply and demand are continually being adjusted throughout the industrial process. ... As in the individual organism, so in the social organism functional equilibrations generate structural equilibrations", etc.[57] And while Marshall could write about "increasing subdivision of functions" in the social organism, etc., as I quoted him earlier, his descriptions of this process are essentially static: they assume a delicately maintained balance of the forces involved. Even if one is prepared to allow for evolutionary change in this balance, as Marshall and Spencer clearly have in mind, there is still the major difficulty in Marshall's writing of an almost contradictory account of the "economic organism" in the main text of *Principles of Economics*, on the one hand, and in the diagrams and mathematics of the Mathemetical Appendix on the other. In fact, according to my colleague, John Nightingale, one can almost talk of an organic, or "biological", account in the main text of the *Principles*, and a mechanical account – as in the machine-like models of the economy in writers like Leon Walras, Vilfredo Pareto and others – in the Mathematical Appendix[58]. Indeed, Marshall himself writes in the Preface to *Principles of Economics*: "the general theory of the equilibrium of demand and supply is a fundamental idea running through the frames of all the various parts of the central problem of Distribution and Exchange".[59]

Of course, a range of views is always healthy, and while Henry George would maintain that "Society is an organism, not a machine",[60] and John Bates Clark would take this literally, there are plenty of economists, especially econometricians, who have little time for biological models. And it must be said that Spencer has not been very helpful here. Currently, as I mentioned earlier, there is an upsurge of interest in evolutionary approaches in economics, but what is meant by the term "evolution" varies considerably. Certainly *Darwinian* evolution is not always the main focus.[61] A paper on "Economics and the Self-Organisation Approach: Alfred Marshall Revisited?" by John Foster, for example, in its first sentence refers to '[s]everal recent contributions in the loosely-defined field of 'evolutionary economics'" which have "focussed upon time irreversibility as the primary source of evolutionary change in economic systems", and has no discussion of Darwin's writings. The paper is largely preoccupied with thermodynamics and the purported relevance of the same for economics, as in the writings of Nicholas Georgescu-Roegen, Ilya Prigogine and others, and it argues that "Marshall was all too aware that no evolutionary economics could be possible until time-irreversibility was properly understood". Foster describes Marshall's own apparent awareness of the tension between equilibrium and stasis in his model of the economy, and his attempts to overcome this through his use of what Foster calls "Spencer's self-organisational process", citing the passage on "Industrial Organisation" I quoted earlier.[62]

Not many economists believe Marshall successfully dealt with his problem, however, and have sought other solutions. Jack Downie in the 1950s, for example, as John Nightingale has shown,[63] endeavoured to move beyond Marshall's "equilibrium, whether in its mechanical or its Spencerian manifestation", and to apply Darwinian competition to Marshall's attempt to reconcile equilibrium with increased returns to scale and monopoly. Marshall's attempt had included utilisation of a famous analogy, the "trees in the forest", out of which he developed the notion of the "representative firm":

> [H]ere we may read a lesson from the young trees of the forest as they struggle upwards through the benumbing shade of their older rivals. Many succumb on the way, and only a few survive; these few become stronger with every year, they get a larger share of light and air with every increase in height, and at last in their turn they tower above their neighbours, and seem as though they would grow on for ever. ... But they do not ... sooner or later age tells on them all. ...
>
> And as with the growth of trees, so it [is] with the growth of businesses as a general rule. ... [A]fter a while, the guidance of [a] business falls into the hands of people with less energy and less creative genius, [and] it is likely

to have lost so much of its elasticity and progressive force, that the advantages are no longer exclusively on its side in its competition with younger and smaller rivals.[64]

Marshall's story implies that at any point in time an industry would be characterised by some firms in an ascending phase and others in a descending one, and "in times of average prosperity *decay in one direction is sure to be balanced by growth in another*"(my italics).[65] Thus Marshall believed he was able to rescue the equilibria of the Mathematical Appendix. Downie, however, disagreed, and cited Marshall's analogy against him as suggesting "more a process of growth and change" than equilibrium. Economies over time change primarily as a result of Darwinian-like competition, Downie held, resulting in the death and extinction of firms (largely due to generation and importation of technical innovations by the successful firms).[66] Such a process *looks*, at any rate, something like natural selection, which, according to Geoff Hodgson, is the essence of Darwinism: "some self-organisation may be an important part of evolution but it cannot replace natural selection".[67]

But competition between firms is not *exactly* Darwinism; it is an analogous process, like Spencer's anatomical analogies of social institutions. And as has often been pointed out, a key difference between Darwinian natural selection in the non-human realm and that which may apply in human social evolution is that the latter manifestly is comparable more with Lamarckian inheritance of acquired characteristics.[68] Humans can pass on learned techniques and abilities to later generations via such non-genetic means as books, and Spencer was of course unapologetically Lamarckian – he saw inheritance of acquired characteristics everywhere, in the biotic and socioeconomic worlds alike.[69] For this, the current growing interest in "evolutionary" economics has much to thank him for, if only in highlighting the perennial need to look beyond disciplinary boundaries when tackling the larger questions of human existence.

Notes and References:

[1] G.M. Hodgson to author, 19 Sept. 2002.

2   J.B. Clark, *The Philosophy of Wealth: Economic Principles Newly Formulated,* Boston, U.S.A., Ginn & Co., 1894, p.38.

3   A. Marshall, *Principles of Economics* (8th edit.), London, Macmillan, 1920, p.769.

4   Ibid.

5   M. Shermer, *In Darwin's Shadow: The Life and Science of Alfred Russel Wallace,* New York, Oxford University Press, 2002, p.239.

6   H. Spencer, *Social Statics, or The Conditions Essential to Human Happiness Specified,* London, Williams and Norgate, 1868, pp.143-4.

7   The quote reads: "It may by-and-by be perceived that equity utters dictates to which we have not yet listened; and men may then learn that to deprive others of their rights to the use of the earth is to commit a crime inferior only in wickedness to the crime of taking away their lives or personal liberties."

8   T. Hogan 'Myths cloud Qld. property rights,' *Queensland Country Life,* 3 April 2003.

9   There are reports of George's lectures in Queensland in the *Brisbane Courier,* 12 May 1890; the *Rockhampton Morning Bulletin,* 16 May 1890; the *Maryborough Chronicle,* 19, 22 May 1890; and the *Gympie Times,* 20 May 1890. (Information supplied by John Pullen.)

10 W.P. Reeves, *State Experiments in Australia and New Zealand* (2 vols), London, George Allen & Unwin Ltd., 1902, Vol I, pp.298-9.

11 Spencer, *Social Statics,* p.132.

12 *Ibid.,* p.141.

13 H.D. Lloyd, *Newest England: Notes of a Democratic Traveller in New Zealand, With some Australian Comparisons,* New York, Doubleday, Page & Co., 1902, p.120.

14 *Qld. Parliamentary Debates* (Legislative Assembly), Vol.XLI, 1883-4, pp.385-403; *Votes and Proceedings of the Legislative Assembly during the Session of 1884 … with the Various Documents connected Therewith,* Vol.III, 1884, Brisbane, Edmund Gregory, Govt. Printer, p.73; R.B. Joyce, 'Samuel Walker Griffith', in D. Murphy, R. Joyce and M. Cribb (eds.), *The Premiers of Queensland,* St. Lucia, Qld., University of Queensland Press, 1990, p.167.

15 R.B. Joyce, *Samuel Walker Griffith,* St. Lucia, Qld., University of Queensland Press, 1984, p.386 (note 66).

16 *Qld. Parliamentary Debates* (Legislative Assembly), Vol. CXXII, 1915-16, pp.2297-8. See also, J.F.N. Murray, *Principles and Practice of Valuation,* Sydney, Comm. Inst. of Valuers, 1966, p.57.

17 Ibid., p.2298.

18 E.G. Theodore, *Policy Speech, 10 Sept. 1920*, Brisbane, Qld., Anthony James Cumming, Govt. Printer, 1920, pp.10-11.

19 Ibid., p.10. See also J.D. Bailey, *A Hundred Years of Pastoral Banking*, Oxford, Clarendon Press, 1966.

20 See D.J. Murphy, 'Edward Granville Theodore', in Murphy et al., *op. cit.* note 14, pp.320 ff.; R. Fitzgerald, *'Red Ted'*, St. Lucia, Qld., University of Qld. Press, 1994, pp.123 ff.

21 Irrigation and Water Supply Commission, *Fifth Annual Report of the Commissioner 1926-27*, Brisbane, Qld., Anthony James Cumming, Govt. Printer, 1927; R.S. Medew, *Dawsonia: A Story of the Dawson Valley Irrigation Scheme*, Yeppoon, Qld., the author, n.d. (c.1975), p.15.

22 Cited in R.F. Skitch, *Encouraging Conservation through Valuation*, (2 vols.), The State of Queensland, Dept. of Natural Resouces, 2000, Vol 1, p.25.

23 Ibid. Clark, an economic advisor to the Queensland Labor government, was apparently much influenced by the distributivist ideas of Hilaire Belloc and G.K. Chesterton. He advocated decentralization, closer settlement of agricultural land and avoidance of industrialization and urban growth. See R. Fitzgerald, *The Pope's Battalions: Santamaria, Catholicism and the Labor Split*, St. Lucia, Qld., University of Queensland Press, 2003, pp.263-4.

24 H. George, *A Perplexed Philosopher, being, An Examination of Mr. Herbert Spencer's Various Utterances on the Land Question, With Some Incidental Reference to his Synthetic Philosophy,* London, Kegan Paul, Trench, Trübner & Co., 1893, p.91.

25 A.R. Wallace, *My Life: A Record of Events and Opinions* (2 vols.), London, Chapman & Hall Ltd., 1908, Vol II, p.30.

26 *Qld. Parliamentary Debates* (Legislative Assembly), vol CXXVII, 1917, p.2203.

27 George, *A Perplexed Philosopher,* p.87.

28 H.G. Wells, *The Work, Wealth and Happiness of Mankind*, London, Heinemann, 1932, p.327. ('Half of Herbert Spencer's writings were an indictment – a fairly sound one – of the contemporary State as a competent receiver'.)

29 George, *A Perplexed Philosopher,* p.91.

30 *Ibid.*

31 H. Spencer, 'Railway Morals and Railway Policy', *Edinburgh Review*, Vol. C (July-Oct 1854), pp.420-61 (459-60).

[32] H. Spencer, 'The Social Organism', *Westminster Review*, New Series Vol. XVII (Jan and April 1860), pp.90-121(96).

[33] T.H. Huxley, 'Administrative Nihilism', in *idem, Method and Results*, New York, Greenwood Press, 1968, pp.251-289 (271)(first published 1871).

[34] S. Webb, 'The Difficulties of Individualism', in M. Taylor (ed.), *Herbert Spencer and the Limits of the State*, Bristol, U.K., Thoemmes Press, 1996, pp. 145-166 (first published 1891).

[35] *Socialist* (Melbourne), 2 April 1906.

[36] H. George, *Progress and Poverty: An Inquiry into the Cause of Industrial Depressions, and of Increase of Want – with Increase of Wealth. The Remedy*, London, Kegan Paul, Trench & Co., 1884, pp.363-4.

[37] J.B. Clark, *Philosophy of Wealth*, p.199.

[38] Ibid, p.38.

[39] Spencer, *Social Statics*, p.141.

[40] H Spencer, 'Specialized Administration', in *idem, Essays: Scientific, Political, and Speculative* (3 vols.), London, Williams and Norgate, 1878, Vol. III, pp.127-170 (133-4).

[41] Ibid., pp.140,150.

[42] Marshall Library of Economics, *Catalogue*, Cambridge, Cambridge University Press, 1927, p.37.

[43] W.E. Hearn, *Plutology, or the Theory of the Efforts to Satisfy Human Wants*, Melbourne, George Robertson, 1863, pp.384-5.

[44] A. Marshall, *Principles of Economics* (4th edit.), London, Macmillan, 1898, pp.319-20.

[45] H. Spencer, *First Principles*, London, Williams and Norgate, 1870, p.346.

[46] *op. cit.* note 42, p.80. Marshall acknowledges the influence of Spencer on his thought in the Preface to *Principles of Economics* (Marshall, *Principles*, 4th ed., p.xii) and in his c.1910 MS essay, 'Alfred Marshall on Himself'(Peter Groenewegen, personal communication). Mary Paley Marshall's vignette about Marshall reading Spencer is in a letter to J.M. Keynes, c. July 1924, JMK papers, King's College, Cambridge (cat. No. EJ/6/4/22-3). Some of Marshall's annotations in his copies of Spencer's books reveal much about his Spencerian view of nature and human society, which was closer to Lamarck than Darwin. For example, against a description by Spencer of the evolution of 'grebe-like habits' in *Puffinuria* in *Principles of Biology* (Vol.1, p.368), Marshall has written: 'Analogies to this may be seen in the growth of mental, moral, social and political conceptions, methods and habits both in the race and the individual.'

[47] P. Groenewegen, *A Soaring Eagle: Alfred Marshall 1842-1924*, Cheltenham, U.K., Edward Elgar, ch.16.

[48] Ibid.

[49] Plato, *The Republic*, Ware, Herts., Wordsworth Editions Ltd., 1997, p.275; P. Pinney, *Who Wanders Alone*, Sydney, Angus and Robertson, 1954, p.70; P. Theroux, *The Happy Isles of Oceana*, London, Penguin, 1992, p.585.

[50] *op. cit.* note 43, p.385.

[51] J.M. Keynes, *A Revision of the Treaty*, London, Macmillan, 1922, p.10.

[52] J.M. Keynes, *Indian Currency and Finance*, London, Macmillan, 1913, p.101; Marshall, *Principles of Economics* (4th edit.), p.72.

[53] See J. Laurent, 'Keynes and Darwinism', in J. Laurent and J. Nightingale (eds.), *Darwinism and Evolutionary Economics*, Cheltenham, U.K., Edward Elgar, 2001, pp.63-84.

[54] J.M. Keynes, *A Treatise on Money*, (2 vols.), London, Macmillan, 1930, Vol.II, pp.406-7.

[55] J.M. Keynes, 'Economic Possibilities for our Grandchildren', *The Nation and Athenaeum*, 11 October 1930, pp.36-7.

[56] This is one of the two editions I happen to possess.

[57] Spencer, *First Principles*, p.508. See also T. Veblen, 'Professor Clark's Economics', in *idem, The Place of Science in Modern Civilization*, New York, Capricorn, 1969 (1908).

[58] J. Nightingale, 'Solving Marshall's Problem with the Biological Analogy: Jack Downie's Competitive Process', in G.M. Hodgson (ed), *Economics and Biology*, Aldershot, Hants., Edward Elgar, 1995, pp.299-318. See also Hodgson's Introduction to this volume.

[59] Marshall, *Principles of Economics* (4th edit.), p.xi.

[60] Quoted in D. Middleton, *The British*, London, Pan Books, 1958, p.72.

[61] See Laurent and Nightingale, *op. cit.* note 53.

[62] J. Foster, 'Economics and the Self-organisation Approach: Alfred Marshall Revisited', *Economic Journal*, Vol. 103 (July 1993), pp.975-991.

[63] *op.cit.* note 58.

[64] Marshall, *Principles of Economics* (8th edit.), pp.315-6.

[65] Ibid., p.317. See also Neil Hart, *The 1920s Cost Controversies: Did Anyone Read Marshall's 'Principles'?* – paper presented at History of Economic Thought Society of Australia Conference, University of New England, Armidale, N.S.W., 16-19 July 2002 (typescript).

[66] *op. cit.* note 58.

[67] G.M. Hodgson, 'Darwinism in Economics: From Analogy to Ontology', *Journal of Evolutionary Economics*, Vol. 12 (2002), pp.259-81 (266).

[68] On the whole question of differences in human evolution, see B. Loasby, *Knowledge, Institutions and Evolution in Economics*, London, Routledge, 2002, chs.2,8.

[69] For Marshall's application of Spencer's Lamarckianism to economics see note 46.

Acknowledgements

Thanks to Greta Jones and Betty Nixon for their kind invitation to participate in this conference, and to Paulette Baxter, Jill Bowie, Geoff Edwards, Timothy Ferguson, Peter Groenewegen, Geoff Hodgson, Gavin Jones, Richard Joseph, Nathan and Rob Laurent, John Marsden, Jim Moore, John Morgan, Robin and Iian Neill, John Nightingale, Peter Pegg, John Pullen, Richard Sanders, Mary Seefried, George and Yvonne Simmons, Rowland Thomas, David and Isabella Thorpe, and the staff of the Queensland State Archives, the John Oxley Memorial Library, Brisbane, the Fryer Library, University of Queensland, and King's College, Cambridge archives for all their help.

5. Herbert Spencer and Altruism: The Sternness and Kindness of a Victorian Moralist

Thomas Dixon

Historians, Scientists, Philosophers and their Herbert Spencers

If you were asked to think of one word or phrase to encapsulate the science and philosophy of that "petty, monotonous, self-pitying, cantankerous" Victorian, Herbert Spencer, memorably once described as "the Eeyore of Victorian science"[1], it is unlikely that "altruism" would be the first word to spring to mind. More likely, you might think of *laissez-faire*, individualism, evolution, survival of the fittest, or perhaps Social Darwinism.[2]   Until relatively recently, Herbert Spencer was normally only mentioned by historians, scientists or philosophers when they wanted to lay hold of a name to stand for the disreputable practice of dressing political ideology up as natural science, and specifically of dressing free-market capitalism up as the theory of evolution.[3] His name became a watchword not only for ideologically tainted science but also for philosophically flawed ethics. Through the influence of the criticisms of the Cambridge moral philosopher Henry Sidgwick and his pupil G.E. Moore, the received wisdom came to be that Spencer's ethics committed the "naturalistic fallacy", conflating scientific descriptions with moral prescriptions. It was hoped that by associating it with terms such as "Social Darwinism", "Herbert Spencer", or "naturalistic fallacy", any project which seemed to cross the divide between the world of evolutionary science on the one hand and the worlds of society, politics and ethics on the other, could be discredited.[4] This was certainly one strategy that was deployed by opponents of E.O. Wilson's sociobiology and Richard Dawkins' selfish gene theory during the 1970s and 1980s.[5]

Central to both Wilson's and Dawkins' projects was the problem of the evolution of altruism. The puzzle of how self-sacrificing individuals could ever have been successful in the merciless struggle for existence was described by Wilson as the "central theoretical problem" of the new discipline which he himself had given the name "sociobiology".[6] And it was Dawkins' stark conclusions on the non-existence of altruism in nature that made his 1976 book *The Selfish Gene* so controversial and compelling. On Dawkins' account we were blind, lumbering robots, programmed by selfish genes. But there was a glimmer of hope. We humans alone, Dawkins said, could rebel against the tyranny of the selfish replicators. "Let us *teach* altruism" he wrote, "because we are born selfish. Let us understand what our selfish genes are up to, because we may then at least have the chance to upset their designs, something that no other species has ever aspired to do".[7] Although Wilson emphasised the naturalness of altruism, and Dawkins the need to rebel against our selfish natures, the commitment to finding an entirely secular, scientific and evolutionary basis upon which to undertake all discussions of human morality was shared by them both. The same commitment has also been made in recent years by philosophical writers inspired by the findings of evolutionary biology, most notably Daniel Dennett, Michael Ruse and Robert Richards, who have all argued since the 1980s for the scientific and philosophical plausibility of evolutionary ethics.[8] To succeed in this argument it was necessary for these writers to have some response to the claims that this was just bad old Spencerian Social Darwinism and fell foul of the naturalistic fallacy.

Among contemporary advocates of evolutionary ethics and evolutionary psychology, there have been differing responses to the Spencer-bashing.[9] Daniel Dennett and Steven Pinker, for instance, simply join in. Dennett enthusiastically condemns the science and the philosophy of "Herbert Spencer and the Social Darwinists", and their misapplications of Darwinian thinking "in defense of political doctrines that range from callous to heinous".[10] Pinker even suggests a direct trajectory from Spencer's ideas about social evolution to the Nazi holocaust.[11]   Michael Ruse is also unenthusiastic[12] but notes cautiously that "Even Herbert Spencer had much to commend him", mentioning particularly his life-long opposition to militarism, which I will come back to below.[13] Robert Richards, however, has taken the most ambitious and direct route of all, attempting at least a partial rehabilitation of Spencer's reputation as an ethicist. In his 1987 book on *Darwin and the Emergence of Evolutionary Theories of Mind and Behavior*, Richards explicitly links this reassessment of Spencer's philosophy with a vigorous defence of the plausibility of evolutionary ethics, and a denial that the naturalistic fallacy is any kind of fallacy at all.[14] Richards acknowledges that Spencer had his flaws, but writes that Spencer's ethics, "in its theoretical structure and ruling imperative must, I believe, be admired".[15] Thus a second Herbert Spencer was born, in some respects the mirror image of the ideologically and philosophically flawed Social Darwinist. This second Spencer undoubtedly expressed some views which were unduly harsh, and was in many ways limited by his own prejudices and those of Victorian Britain more generally. However his logic was essentially sound and he is to be celebrated as a pioneer not only of evolutionary psychology but also of evolutionary ethics.

This idea of Spencer's importance as a pioneer of evolutionary approaches to ethics would seem to be strengthened still further by the recognition that he was, as I will explain below, in large part responsible for the acceptance of the very terms "altruism" and "altruistic" into the English language. Three works of Spencer's, published in the 1870s, made extensive use of these neologisms; namely the second edition of *The Principles of Psychology* (1870-2), *The Study of Sociology* (1873), and *The Data of Ethics* (1879). Spencer described how altruistic sentiments and forms of conduct had evolved and the ways that they could and should be encouraged if society was to reach its ideal state, in which altruism would be voluntary and spontaneous. He wrote about the respective roles of natural selection and inheritance of acquired habits – or, to use the familiar shorthand, Darwinian and Lamarckian mechanisms of evolution – in producing human altruism, and compared the manifestations of altruism in more and less civilised societies.[16] And he argued that ethics should be seen as both a science of conduct and a source of moral obligation. All of these would seem to make the second Herbert Spencer, the patron saint of evolutionary ethics, seem an ever more plausible figure.

What I hope to show in this paper, however, is that there are many more than two Herbert Spencers. The well-known Spencer, of course, is the apparently merciless advocate of the operation of survival of the fittest within society as well as within nature, as the mechanism of progress towards the ideal social state. One can find plenty of examples of this Spencer. This is the Spencer who, when writing on the question of what duty of beneficence was owed to the sick and the injured, could argue that the moral character and the social value of the potential beneficiary should be weighed up by the potential benefactor before deciding whether to offer help or not. "If as much sacrifice is made for the sick good-for-nothing as is made for the sick good-for-something," this Spencer wrote, "there is abolished one of those distinctions between the results of good and bad conduct which all should strive to maintain. ... Much more may rightly be done for one whose abilities or energies promise public benefit, than for one who is useless to his fellow-men, or is a burden on them".[17] Whether this would count for Dennett as "callous" or as "heinous", quotations such as this could be multiplied almost indefinitely. This hard-hearted Spencer is well known. Perhaps less well known are the Spencers I want to focus on below, such as Spencer the altruist and Spencer the passionate pacifist.

There is much to learn, then, about Spencer, about Victorian moralism, and about the philosophy of altruism, by looking beyond the images of Spencer created both by proponents and opponents of evolutionary ethics. What these have in common is the centrality they give to evolutionary science on the one hand and to the logic of ethics on the other. These reconstructions do not capture the full range of the genres and subject-matter encompassed by the corpus of Spencer's writings. The parts of the *Synthetic Philosophy* dealing with ethics contain some passages which are clearly recognisable by modern standards as theoretical speculations in biology, psychology, sociology or philosophy. Others plunder empirical data from the writings of historians, anthropologists, and authors of travellers' tales. There are many parts, however, which are more self-help than science, more propaganda than philosophy, more sermonising than sociology. To understand those, we need to read Spencer's ethics in the context of Victorian Britain, its empire, its religion and its politics.

In what follows, I cannot presume to reveal a singular "real" Herbert Spencer, nor to adjudicate on the question of whether "evolutionary ethicist" or "Social Darwinist" is a more appropriate designation. I hope I can, though, at least offer a few alternative insights into the man and his work. I will focus especially on Spencer's combination of sternness towards the undeserving poor at home with kindness towards the victims of British imperialism abroad; and on the way that his views on altruism were shaped by his opposition to a range of other religious and political projects. He objected not only to the hypocrisies of the Christian establishment; but also to the hot-headed and unconsidered philanthropy of socialists and communists that he saw on all sides as the century wore on; and, finally, he objected to the philosophy and religion of Auguste Comte and his British followers. It is with Comte and the positivists that the story of the invention of altruism begins.

Auguste Comte, the Religion of Humanity, and the Discourse of Altruism

Looking at the introduction of the discourse of altruism, by which I mean the family of terms, "altruism", "altruistic" and "altruist", into the English language between the 1850s and 1870s provides a fascinating example of the way that, to quote James Moore, a textured analysis of contested terms can reveal how "*language* maps cultural change".[18] There already existed, of course, a plethora of similar terms used within nineteenth-century moral and religious discourses, terms such as sympathy, benevolence, self-sacrifice, philanthropy, charity, or simply love. What, then, was the attraction of the new discourse of "altruism"?[19] Why would somebody – particularly Herbert Spencer – favour this new discourse over established terminology?

Spencer's adoption of the neologisms "altruism" and "altruistic", like his adoption of the new terms "sociology" and "social statics", was something of a double-edged sword. All of these terms were taken from the writings of the French positivist and sociologist, Auguste Comte.[20] (Comte had first used the term *altruisme*, in the first volume of his *Système de Politique Positive*, in 1851.) On the one hand, using this Comtean language could mark Spencer out as somebody in touch with new, scientific ways of thinking, untainted by old theological superstitions or metaphysical abstractions. On the other hand, however, it was this adoption of the language of Comte and the positivists, this wearing of their philosophical clothes, if you like, which led to the constant perception, by both friends and foes of Comte's philosophy, that Herbert Spencer was himself a follower of Comte.[21]   This was an allegation which Spencer resisted vigorously throughout his life, sometimes going to quite extraordinary lengths to prove his lack of dependence on Comte, including publishing, in 1864, an appendix to his *Classification of the Sciences*, entitled simply "Reasons for Dissenting from the Philosophy of M. Comte".[22]

Spencer might have been better advised, if he had really wished to distinguish his own philosophical and political projects very clearly from those of Comte and the positivists, to have steered clear of the language of altruism. The term "altruism" was first used in an English-language publication in 1852. This was a review of Comte's *Positive Polity*, written by Spencer's friend, later the partner of George Eliot, G.H. Lewes. Lewes described "altruism" as "a felicitous phrase coined by Comte".[23]   Other early users of the term in the 1850s and 1860s included George Eliot, John Stuart Mill, and the philosopher and aural surgeon James Hinton.[24]   The term "altruism" was, when Spencer started to use it, firmly associated not only with Comte's positivist philosophy and sociology but also with the Religion of Humanity. This religion was the central focus of Comte's vision of society in the *Positive Polity*, which was subtitled "A Treatise of Sociology, instituting the Religion of Humanity". This was a fully-fledged religion, with Comte as its high priest, a catechism, liturgies, hymns, and calendars of saints; Thomas Huxley famously summarised it as "Catholicism *minus* Christianity".[25]   In Britain, Frederic Harrison and Richard Congreve were the leading lights of the Comtean religion, which, especially from the 1860s to 1880s, tapped into the desire, felt among a certain kind of young Victorian, for a humanistic religion of altruism combined with a scientific programme for social reform. There were centres of positivist religion, with their own chapels and temples of humanity, in London, Oxford, Manchester, Newcastle and Liverpool.[26] The social investigators Charles Booth and Beatrice Potter (later Beatrice Webb), and even Spencer's arch-critic Henry Sidgwick, had all flirted with the Comtean religion in their youth.[27]

And just in case any of his readers failed to make the connection between the language of altruism and the religion and philosophy of Auguste Comte, Spencer himself explicitly acknowledged the Comtean pedigree of the term "altruistic" when he first used it in the second edition of the *Principles of Psychology*:

> I gladly adopt this word, for which we are indebted to M. Comte. Not long since, some critic, condemning it as new-fangled, asked why we should not be content with such good old-fashioned words as benevolent and beneficent. There is a quite-sufficient reason. Altruism and altruistic, suggesting by their forms as well as their meanings the antitheses of egoism and egoistic, bring quickly and clearly into thought the opposition in a way that benevolence or beneficence and its derivatives do not, because the antitheses are not directly implied by them. This superior suggestiveness greatly facilitates the communication of ethical ideas.[28]

The critic whom Spencer probably had in mind when he wrote this, in 1872, was the Anglican clergyman and philologist, Frederic W. Farrar. (Who better than a philologist to recognise the cultural significance of linguistic innovations?) Delivering the Hulsean lectures in Cambridge in 1870, Farrar referred to the devotees of Comte's Religion of Humanity, and their motto: "Live for others". This was indeed a grand motto, Farrar told his Cambridge audience, but, he asked them "Is 'altruism' a sweeter or better word than charity?"[29] Spencer's answer, in 1872 at least, was "yes".

Spencer's enthusiastic use of the new terminology continued throughout the 1870s. His popular 1873 work, *The Study of Sociology*, had initially been published in instalments in the *Contemporary Review*, and subsequently came out in the same International Scientific Series as works such as John William Draper's *History of the Conflict between Religion and Science* (1875), and Spencer's friend Thomas H. Huxley's *The Crayfish: An Introduction to the Study of Zoology* (1880). In the *Study of Sociology*, Spencer contrasted the primitive religion of enmity with the religion of amity, or "the religion of unqualified altruism".[30] His message, as so often in his philosophy, was that a compromise or conciliation needed to be struck between the two extremes.

In addition to both Christianity and the Religion of Humanity, as examples of religions advocating excessive altruism, Spencer, in the *Data of Ethics* (1879), turned to the utilitarianism of Bentham and Mill. Here he developed further the theme of the need for a conciliation between egoism and altruism, and accused the utilitarians of promoting an ideology of "pure altruism". Reviewers differed in their responses to this, but one theme which came up repeatedly was Spencer's relationship to Comte. Writing in the *Princeton Review*, the Calvinist Scot, Princeton President James McCosh, wrote: "I prefer the phrase 'love' to altruism, the Comtean one, which the school is seeking to introduce, inasmuch as the former demands an inward affection whereas the latter might be satisfied by an outward act".[31] Being represented as a member of the Comtean "school" would have infuriated Spencer, as would the Cambridge moralist Henry Sidgwick's allegation that Spencer was getting confused between utilitarianism and Comtism. Sidgwick wrote, in *Mind*, that Spencer's apparent antagonism to the Utilitarian school depended "on a mere misunderstanding" and that "his quarrel is not really with the very sober and guarded 'altruism' of Bentham and the Benthamites, but with certain hard sayings of the prophet of the Positivist religion, from whom the term Altruism is taken".[32]

When Spencer wrote "altruism", his readers read "Comte", and this led to genuine confusions.[33] Spencer and Comte agreed about many things. They looked forward to a future society where barbarous, militarised forms of society would be replaced by civilised, industrialised ones marked by greater altruism.[34] In this process both expected to see theological dogmas increasingly replaced by scientific facts, and to see God replaced by Humanity as the ultimate focus of men's moral strivings. They both believed in the universal reign of natural law, and interpreted natural laws as empirical generalisations of observed phenomena. They both wrote turgid, multi-volume, jargon-packed philosophical syntheses and proposed their own classification of the sciences. Both held the sciences of sociology and ethics to be the most important of all. But for all these similarities, when it came to the most important question – how was "the millennial state of *altruism*"[35] to be brought about? – Comte and Spencer had diametrically opposed views. The revolutionary triad of liberty, equality and fraternity were replaced in Comte's positivist manifesto by the mantra "Love, Order, Progress". The ideal society proposed by Comte in his *Positive Polity* was, in effect, run by a form of highly organised social management, in which the liberty and equality of individual citizens was sacrificed for the sake of enforced fraternity, and orderly scientific and industrial progress. This society would be rigidly hierarchical, ruled from above by secular and spiritual leaders.[36] This was the opposite of Spencer's dream of an ever diminishing role for government and a form of spontaneous co-operation which maintained a maximum of individual freedom. So, despite the many similarities, Spencer was at least partly right when he protested, for the umpteenth time, in his autobiography that his adoption of Comtean language did not imply adherence to Comtean philosophy or religion. "Save in the adoption of his word 'altruism,' which I have defended," Spencer wrote, "and in the adoption of his word 'sociology,' because there was no other available word (for both which adoptions I have been blamed), the only indebtedness I recognize is the indebtedness of antagonism".[37]

Spencer's failure to shake off the tags "Comtean" and "positivist" illustrated just how intimate a connection there was, both for writers and for readers, between changes in terminology and changes in doctrine. Such changes in terminology, as I have already said, also mapped broader cultural and political changes.

What, then, were the most significant connections between Spencer's psychological and sociological theories of altruism and Victorian domestic and political life?

Spencer on Altruism in the 1870s: Conceptual Problems and Worldly Concerns

Spencer's *Principles of Psychology* was first published in 1855, before Spencer had even conceived of the ten-volume *Synthetic Philosophy* of which it was to become a part. The conception of the *Synthetic Philosophy* in late 1857, the execution of which was to become the single ruling purpose of Spencer's life, and the publication in 1859 of Darwin's *On the Origin of Species*, both meant that when it came to producing a second edition of the *Principles of Psychology*, a large amount of rewriting and of new material were required. The first volume of the second edition came out in 1870, the second in 1872. It was in the second volume, in a new chapter of "Corollaries", that Spencer first wrote about the psychology of the "altruistic" sentiments, introducing the section with the acknowledgement of the term's origins which was quoted above.

The "altruistic" sentiments comprised one of three related groups of moral feelings, the "egoistic", the "ego-altruistic" and the "altruistic". All of these were classed as sentiments as opposed to appetites or instincts by virtue of resulting from higher cognitive representations and re-representations (to use Spencer's ghastly terminology) of more basic feelings and impulses. The egoistic sentiments were those which were related to personal welfare and happiness, such as the remembrance of past pleasures, the love of acquisition and possession, and the resistance of restraints on conduct.[38] The ego-altruistic sentiments were those feelings which gave rise to seemingly altruistic behaviour but which in reality arose from the recognition of personal benefits which would accrue from such behaviour – benefits such as the approval of others, or rewards in this world or the next. Thus consciousness of right and wrong took its origins in such ego-altruistic feelings, and the standards of right and wrong arising from these feelings would vary widely from place to place depending on "the theological traditions and social circumstance" that prevailed; in other words, depending on the moral tastes of the local leaders, ancestor or gods.[39] Finally, the altruistic sentiments, which were increasingly in evidence in "the philanthropy of modern times", and which would prevail in the perfect social state of the future, were evolved from the ego-altruistic sentiments, and "not sharply marked off" from them.[40] All altruistic feelings were "sympathetic excitements of egoistic feelings", whether those feelings were sea-sicknesses, the urge to yawn, or sentiments proper, such as the love of possession, which could be sympathetically felt as the altruistic sentiment of generosity.[41]

Spencer's 1872 treatment of altruism, then, focussed on the altruistic feelings and sentiments which would be increasingly felt as the "predatory" form of social life gave way to the "industrial". Now that life was less painful, he thought, the altruistic sentiments, "which find their satisfaction in conduct that is regardful of others and so conduces to harmonious co-operation", would become ever stronger.[42] In his focus on sentiments (rather than on behaviour); in his view that the two roots of these sentiments were to be found in the basic human capacities of sympathy and parental instinct; and in his belief that these sentiments would gain in strength as society developed, Spencer echoed the teachings of Comte on the subject. For Comte, the great problem of human life had been how to subordinate the egoistic feelings to the altruistic, and it was through studying the laws of life, mind and society (through the sciences of biology, phrenology and sociology) that one could come to understand how that subordination might be achieved. Comte also made use of the distinction between earlier military and later industrial modes of social existence.[43]

For all these similarities between Spencer's and Comte's treatments of altruistic feelings, there were important differences too. While Comte envisaged these sentiments being maximised in an autocratic society in which the autocrat was Auguste Comte, Spencer envisaged them coming about increasingly in a freely co-operating society of individuals, in which the individuals were all Herbert Spencer. For, eventually, on Spencer's model, as the altruistic sentiments, through being associated with the sympathetic pleasures that they produced, became stronger, there would arise individuals so advanced that their altruistic sentiments would "begin to call into question the authority of the ego-altruistic sentiments" – that is the love of approval and reward which earlier theological systems had played upon. Those men who were prepared to "brave the frowns of their fellows by pursuing courses at variance with old but injurious customs, and even cause dissent from the current religion", would eventually come to dominate in the ideal future state.[44] It would be a brave new world of morally unimpeachable but unbelieving altruists.

At the same time that Spencer had been working on the second edition of his *Principles of Psychology*, Darwin had produced his two major works on human evolution, *The Descent of Man* (1871) and *The Expression of the Emotions in Man and* Animals (1872). In these works, Darwin had proposed his account of how other-regarding sentiments could have evolved through a mixture of inheritance of acquired traits, sexual selection and natural selection operating between communities.[45] Spencer's creation of a system of evolutionary ethics, however, while similar in some respects to Darwin's own speculations, went well beyond theorising about the evolutionary origins of moral feelings. In fact, Spencer's treatment of the subject was at the same time both more philosophically abstract and more connected to the mundane world of Victorian domestic and political life than Darwin's. The details of this treatment first came to public notice in 1879, when Spencer published the first part of his *Principles of Ethics*, the part of his *Synthetic Philosophy* which he regarded as the cornerstone of the whole system. The unassuming title of the work was *The Data of Ethics*. Approximately a quarter of the book was about the relationship between egoism and altruism, in chapters entitled "Egoism *versus* Altruism", "Altruism *versus* Egoism", "Trial and Compromise", and "Conciliation". The central note of the untenability of either extreme egoism or extreme altruism was the same one that had been struck in the *Principles of Psychology* and the *Study of Sociology*. Spencer sought now to blur the boundary between the two categories. He argued that effective altruism could not be undertaken without taking care, egoistically, to look after one's own mental and bodily well-being and that of one's family; and that altruism, in any case, had many egoistic benefits, such as the pleasure it could bring to the benefactor and the broader rewards of living in a co-operative society.

Robert Richards, as I noted above, has provided an immensely thorough and sympathetic reassessment of Spencer's ethics as a valuable and pioneering contribution to the enterprise of evolutionary ethics.[46] There is no need for me to replicate that exposition and analysis here. What I would like to do instead is draw attention to two different features of the *Data of Ethics*, especially as they relate to the subject of altruism. The first is to do with conceptual problems, the second to do with the examples Spencer chose to illustrate his philosophical arguments.

So, first, what were the conceptual problems? To this day, philosophical and theological debates about altruism are plagued by definitional and conceptual confusions about what "altruism" means.[47] These were exacerbated by Richard Dawkins' use in *The Selfish Gene* of two different senses of altruism – biological altruism which is defined in terms of fitness and, he contends, does not exist in nature; and moral altruism which is defined in terms of motivations and is something that we should teach our children.[48] This confusion between biological definitions that focus on observable behaviours and outcomes on the one hand and ethical definitions that focus on feelings and intentions on the other was introduced into discussions of the topic almost exactly one hundred years before Dawkins' intervention, however. The culprit was Herbert Spencer. His initial definition of altruism was quite straightforward. Altruism was to be defined as "all action which, in the normal course of things, benefits others instead of benefiting self".   This was to include all "acts by which offspring are preserved and the species maintained", in non-human as well as human species, and regardless of whether there was any conscious motivation; "acts of automatic altruism" were to be included along with those motivated by a desire to help others.[49] As with Dawkins in the 1970s, Spencer in the 1870s took pleasure in thinking that some, who thought altruism meant simply "conscious sacrifice of self to others among human beings", would find his extension of the definition of altruism so far beyond that meaning, to include the lowest forms of life, to be counter-intuitive or absurd. Where Dawkins more recently reduced the discussion of altruism to the level of genetic material, Spencer reduced altruism to those actions which "involved a loss of bodily substance".[50] Spencer's vision and Dawkins' differ significantly only in that Spencer presented the evolution of life as a process in which egoism and altruism, defined in his reductive biological senses, were both primordial (although egoism was primary), and evolved simultaneously.

This extension of altruism to all acts that benefited others, undertaken by any creature, and which involved the loss of bodily substance, would perhaps have been contrary to what most thought would be a natural definition of altruism in the 1870s, but in itself it entailed no particular conceptual difficulties. The difficulties were caused by the fact that Spencer had, both in his earlier works and in the *Data of Ethics* itself, either tacitly or explicitly used different definitions of altruism; definitions which focussed on feelings rather than actions, motivations rather than outcomes. Those other-regarding actions that were motivated by the love of praise or rewards, by the second-rate "ego-altruistic" sentiments of the *Principles of Psychology*, now seemed to qualify as straightforwardly altruistic, since a benefit to others was now the only requirement for that title. In the *Data of Ethics*, Spencer sometimes stuck with his initial definition in terms of actions, but at other times he applied the adjective "altruistic" to a sort of motive, a type of character, a sort of sympathetic feeling (as he had in the *Principles of Psychology*), or even to a philosophical doctrine or ideology (as in his allegation that utilitarianism was a form of "pure altruism"). Reviewers picked up on this from the outset. McCosh's remark that he preferred "love" which implied inward affection to Comtean "altruism" which might simply refer to an outward act alluded to the problem.[51] Alfred W. Benn, reviewing the work for *Mind* in 1880, identified it more directly. He complained that what Spencer meant by altruism was unclear, and suggested that words ending in -ism "never denote actions but always beliefs or dispositions". Altruism then should mean, not a sort of action, but "the feeling that prompts us to benefit others … which is not quite the same thing". Benn also rightly noted that

Spencer introduced further confusion by talking about the pleasurable feelings arising from actions benefiting others as "altruistic pleasures". This was misleading since these feelings certainly were not themselves of any benefit to others. Spencer was equivocating between "altruistic" and "sympathetic". [52] From its earliest uses as a central term in evolutionary ethics, with both biological and moral connotations, the word "altruism" was beset by definitional problems.

The second feature of Spencer's writing about altruism in the *Data of Ethics* that I want to bring out is his use of examples. These examples, from inattentive chambermaids to the effort to stamp out the slave trade, which would have helped to bring out the implications of his arguments for himself and his readers, normally vanish in standard secondary accounts of Spencer's sociology and philosophy. The supposition, presumably, is that they do not form a significant part of his writings, since they are not central to the conceptual framework. In fact the opposite is true. These examples often reveal the real message of Spencer's philosophy as well as its deepest motivations. Eliminating the references Spencer made to Victorian domestic and political life does not help us to see his philosophical arguments more clearly, rather it makes them seem abstract and bloodless. Like all good moral philosophy, Spencer's ethics was about how an individual can live a good life and how society can be changed for the better. Such a philosophy must engage with the realities of individual and collective living, not just with abstract arguments, and it is to Spencer's credit that his did so, whatever we think of his conclusions. Let me offer just two illustrations of this.

In the chapter on "Altruism *versus* Egoism", Spencer argued that to act altruistically was in each individual's own private interest as well as in the general interest. The bodily and mental well-being of one's fellow-citizen had a direct impact on one's own happiness. Each man could understand this, Spencer said, by thinking just about his own household and about the servants and workmen he employed. There he could see for himself the ways in which the physical, mental and moral deficiencies of others could cause him inconvenience and distress.

> Unpunctuality and want of system are perpetual sources of annoyance. The unskilfulness of the cook causes frequent vexation and occasional indigestion. Lack of forethought in the housemaid leads to a fall over a bucket in a dark passage. And inattention to a message or forgetfulness in delivering it, entails failure in an important engagement.[53]

Similarly Spencer asked his reader to think about the frequent damage done by incompetent and dishonest builders and plumbers, and especially by those who set themselves a low standard of work on "the unionist principle that the better workers must not discredit the worse by exceeding them in efficiency", which in turn was produced by "the immoral belief that the unworthy should fare as well as the worthy". All of this went to show that "the improvement of others, physically, intellectually, and morally, personally concerns each" and that we would all benefit egoistically "by such altruism as aids in raising the average intelligence". The question of how to achieve this was a separate matter. Spencer was an opponent of state education, which "taxes ratepayers that children's minds may be filled with dates, and names, and gossip about kings, and narratives of battles, and other useless information". [54] He had his own views about private charity and education, which do not concern us here.[55] The point is that Spencer's philosophical writings on ethics were as much about lazy plumbers, incompetent cooks, trades unions and state education as they were about the Kantian categorical imperative or the doctrines of utilitarianism.

Although Herbert Spencer's attitudes to the undeserving poor, not to mention to his own servants, seem to us quite merciless, his views regarding the proper treatment of "alien peoples" and "inferior races" were altogether more sympathetic. Altruism between individuals in Victorian society should be, Spencer thought, strictly limited so as to avoid multiplying the dependent and degenerate classes still further. Between nations, however, Spencer insisted that altruism needed to be increased dramatically and urgently. One of the themes that came up most consistently in Spencer's writings on beneficence and altruism, from the *Social*

Statics of 1851 onwards, was the connection between foreign policy and moral sentiments. The argument was that progress could only be made towards a more freely co-operative and altruistic society internally when external relations were peaceful; when barbarous militancy had evolved into civilised industrialism; when war had been replaced by mutually beneficial trade. In his writings on altruism in the early 1870s Spencer had already identified the apparent conflict between egoism and altruism with the contrast between the predatory and the industrial regimes, and between the religions of enmity and amity. Now, in the *Data of Ethics*, Spencer used examples of British imperial iniquities in order to persuade readers simultaneously of the connections between international and domestic morality and of the hypocrisy of the current established religion. Again, Spencer's abstract ethical philosophy subserved a mundane political goal: the goal of furthering the causes of pacifism and secularism.

It was on this subject of the hypocrisies of the British Empire that Spencer was at his most eloquent. He wrote of the "unscrupulous greed of conquest cloaked by pretences of spreading the blessings of British rule and British religion" and explained how this aggressive foreign policy increased government expenditure and paralysed international trade. He criticised those of the industrial classes who "thinking themselves unconcerned in our doings abroad, are suffering from lack of that wide-reaching altruism which should insist on just dealings with other peoples, civilized or savage".[56] But his most passionate polemic was saved for the bishops, especially those who had seats in the House of Lords and were thus directly implicated in government policy. Citing as an example, the brutal response to the murder of Bishop John Coleridge Patteson in Melanesia in 1871, Spencer wrote that the British government had gone even further than the primitive rule of a life for a life and developed the rule "For one life many lives".[57] Spencer regretted that his new pacifistic and evolutionary view of ethics would not appeal to "those whose reverence for one who told them to put up the sword is shown by using the sword to spread his doctrine among the heathens"; nor to the "ten thousand priests of the religion of love, who are silent when the nation is moved by the religion of hate"; nor to the bishops who, "far from urging the extreme precept of the master they pretend to follow, to turn the other cheek when one is smitten, vote for acting on the principle – strike lest ye be struck". In this moralistic peroration, Spencer rammed home the message that those who believed that a rationalised version of Christian ethical principles could be applied while rejecting the Christian creed, were altogether morally superior to these "men who profess Christianity and practise Paganism".[58]

Through Spencer's influence, then, the language of altruism spread rapidly during the 1870s, and continued to have both anti-Christian and scientific connotations. It continued for many to be associated with Comte and positivism, not least because, rightly or wrongly, Spencer himself was so associated. In Spencer's own discussions the same optimism about a more altruistic future society, in which traditional religious beliefs would be rejected, consolidated the status of "altruism" as an ideal of the scientific agnostic, the moralising doubter, the respectable unbeliever.

Socialism and Spencer's Retreat from Altruism in the 1890s

In the early 1870s, Spencer had been one of the very first writers, other than G.H. Lewes, George Eliot, and John Stuart Mill, to adopt the language of "altruism". By the early 1890s, when he finally produced the rest of his *Principles of Ethics* (of which the *Data of Ethics* had been just one of the six projected parts), the term and its cognates were in general use. This was testified to by Spencer's friend and disciple, the agnostic popular science writer, Grant Allen, in 1894. The editor of the publication *Science Gossip* had approached several eminent personages, including Allen, to ask their opinions about the propriety or otherwise of the term "scientist". Allen responded that, personally, he disliked the word scientist, but that he recognised that languages grew "irresponsibly" and that if the majority of people adopted a word, little could be done about it. "We have swallowed 'Sociology'," he wrote, "we have swallowed 'Altruism' and I don't see why, after camels like those, we need strain at a comparative gnat like 'Scientist'".[59] There can be little doubt that it was the adoption of these Comtean "camels" by Herbert Spencer, who was widely regarded both as the leading English philosopher of the age and the chief exponent of evolution, which did more than any other single factor to ensure that they were "swallowed" in both Britain and America. As noted above, the adoption of these two words was the full extent of the debt that Spencer was prepared to acknowledge to Comte, although others could not accept that he adopted so much Comtean terminology without having absorbed any of the doctrine.[60]

This issue of Spencer's dependence on Comte refused to go away. It had come to the fore again in 1884 in the context of an extended spat between Spencer and one of the leading positivists of the day, Frederic Harrison. In January, Spencer published an article on religion in the *Nineteenth Century*, to which Harrison responded in the March issue. Harrison criticised Spencer's description of the unknowable ultimate reality as "an Infinite and Eternal Energy, from which all things proceed"' as an unnecessarily grandiose and theological formulation of what could simply have been designated "the unknown".[61] Then in September the two clashed again, in the pages of the *Times*, over claims made by Harrison in an address on "The Memory of Auguste Comte and his True Work", which was reprinted in the *Times*. Harrison had described Spencer's philosophy as "nothing but an attempt to play a new tune on Comte's instrument". This led to an exchange of published letters to the editor from Spencer and Harrison, each penning their claims in the rooms of the gentleman's club to which they both belonged, the *Athenaeum*. Spencer went over the old ground, already covered in his 1864 pamphlet, and added to this the testimony of a letter from John Stuart Mill supporting his independence from Comte. Central to Harrison's reply was the claim that Spencer, by adopting Comtean terminology, implicitly adopted parts of the doctrine too. It was Harrison's view that "terms which crystallize entire modes of thought are of crucial import". The terms he had in mind included sociology, social evolution, social environment and social organism. These were "terms of art" introduced by Comte as early as 1839, and yet Spencer, he said "can hardly write a page without employing them;

and employing also, as I hold, the conception of Comte". The same was true, Harrison went on, "of what Mr Spencer writes about 'altruism' in ethics, and about an industrial succeeding to a military organization in sociology". Harrison's conclusion was that Spencer, through his long association and friendship with the two Comtean Georges, Lewes and Eliot, had unconsciously appropriated more than he had realised of the positivist philosophy. Spencer's response contained nothing new, and on the question of the term altruism he simply conceded again that the word was indeed Comte's and that it was "a very useful word".[62]

The reappearance in 1884 of these allegations of unconscious appropriation, which centred around his borrowing of Comtean terms including "altruism", was one of two factors which made the term a much less attractive one to Spencer in the 1890s than it had been in the 1870s. The other principal factor was the increasing association of the term, during the 1880s and 1890s, with various ideologies of which he distinctly disapproved, especially Christianity, socialism and communism. In 1883, when preaching the sermon at the funeral of Queen Victoria's attendant, John Brown, for instance, the Bishop of Ripon had taken as his subject, "Christian Altruism".[63] An article in the *Spectator* in 1892, entitled "The Extravagance of Altruism", complained about "the exaggerated altruism of which we hear so much now on all sides" and the consequent neglect of one's own proper interests which was being advocated.[64] By 1897, the *Spectator* perceived the existence of a fanatical new creed of "universal altruism" which, they warned, would mean in practice "a universe of spoilt children, a wilderness of men tended, protected, watched over, and cosseted until there is nothing in them but a constant expectation of favour and defence from all above or around them". The same article ridiculed the idea that Christ had taught altruism in the same way that it was taught by those who had accepted the "Socialist theory now so prevalent". This assault on socialistic altruism concluded as follows:

> "England," said Nelson, "expects every man to do his duty." "And mine too," whimpers the devotee of altruism, who even when he works faithfully for another

expects ten men to work for him. Are all the masculine
virtues to disappear in one rush of motherliness?[65]

The following year, one of the very sort of people that the
Spectator had thus derided, the journalist and socialist campaigner
Robert Blatchford, wrote a pamphlet entitled "Altruism: Christ's
Glorious Gospel of Love Against Man's Dismal Science of Greed",
in which he argued that socialism was bound to succeed since it
was supported by "the strongest sentiment of modern times – the
sentiment of human love and mercy called Altruism".[66] It would
be fair to assume that Spencer had more sympathy with the
damning tones of the *Spectator* than he did with the sentimental
Christian socialism of Blatchford and his ilk.

So Spencer himself, in the *Principles of Ethics* (1892-3), in order to
dissociate himself both from Comtism and from socialism, and in a
tacit acknowledgement of the irresponsible ways in which the
terms' meanings had grown and changed, greatly reduced his uses
of "altruism" and "altruistic". Instead he generally preferred the
terms "beneficence" and "beneficent" (the very terms which he
had compared unfavourably with "altruism" and "altruistic" twenty
years earlier). The explicit reason that Spencer gave for his new
terminology was that there was a tendency to overlook important
distinctions between different kinds of altruistic conduct.[67]
Spencer insisted on one distinction in particular, which he
embodied in the titles of parts 5 and 6 of the *Principles of Ethics*:
"Negative Beneficence" and "Positive Beneficence". Negative
beneficence involved self-restraint in one's dealings with fellow
citizens; in short it meant respecting their equal rights to justice in
social and economic interactions.   Positive beneficence, or
generosity, involved, where appropriate, actively promoting the
welfare of one's spouse, parents, children, the sick, the poor and
the injured. Although the introduction of this useful conceptual
distinction was, then, Spencer's superficial reason for replacing the
overly-broad "altruism" with negative and positive "beneficence",
he surely also wished to distance himself from the new sentimental
creed of altruism. He was unremittingly critical of the prevalent
"hot-headed philanthropy, impatient of criticism", which ignored
the distinction between justice and generosity and which was, "by

helter-skelter legislation destroying normal connexions between conduct and consequence". The end result of this indiscriminate altruism would be the creation of a state "having for its motto the words: – It shall be as well for you to be inferior as to be superior". "Indiscriminate philanthropy", Spencer feared, was leading to a discouragement of industry amongst the poor and, through the fostering of the idle and dissolute and their offspring, to a bodily and mental degeneration of the race.[68]

Spencer had written, in June 1892, in the preface to the first volume of the *Principles of Ethics*, that he was anxious to get to work on the composition of parts 5 and 6, on positive and negative beneficence, which would appear in the second volume, before his strength finally failed him. Without them, he feared, the parts which had been published so far would leave "a very erroneous impression respecting the general tone of evolutionary ethics". In its full form, he said, "the moral system to be set forth unites sternness with kindness; but thus far attention has been drawn almost wholly to the sternness".[69] The reader of parts 5 and 6, however, when they were published the following year, would have searched in vain for this promised kindness. Spencer's prioritisation of the health of society over the health of the individual, combined with his belief in the inheritance of acquired mental and moral traits, always led to what sounded simply like more sternness. The greatest difficulty, Spencer felt, when it came to relief of the poor (one of the principal kinds of positive beneficence), was how to "regulate our pecuniary beneficence" so as to "avoid assisting the incapables and the degraded" in multiplying.[70] And this difficulty seemed to Spencer "almost insurmountable". As a result he was as stern as ever. He blamed unconsidered state-funded philanthropy for having brought into existence large numbers who were "unadapted to social life" and simply "sources of misery to themselves and others". The only way that this "body of relatively worthless people" could be diminished was through the inflicting of pain: "Cure can come only through affliction". The affliction he had in mind was the pain that would be endured in the transition from a condition of "State-beneficence" to one of "self-help and private beneficence".[71] If there was any solution, Spencer wrote, then that was the only one he could think of. His earlier optimism about the prospects of a more civilised and altruistic society evolving seemed quite shattered. Even his faith in the all-encompassing principle of evolution had been shaken by now. In the preface to the second volume of the work he wrote words that none of his friends or foes could have expected ever to hear from him: "The Doctrine of Evolution has not furnished guidance to the extent that I hoped".[72]

So by the 1890s Spencer had retreated from both the language and the optimism of his earlier writings on altruism. He became ever sterner in the limits he felt must be placed on beneficence towards the morally, mentally and physically inferior. One of the elements that remained consistent with his earlier writings, however, was his condemnation of British military "brigandage" and the hypocrisy of Christian leaders. Both in the *Principles of Ethics* and in the final volume of the *Principles of Sociology*, which, on its publication in 1896 marked the completion of the *Synthetic Philosophy*, Spencer's pacifism and anti-Christianity still shone through. He continued to write about the contradictions and hypocrisies involved in British society as a result of its professed adherence to a religion of amity combined with its practical acting out of a religion of enmity. Every day, he said, provided more examples of the resulting contradictions, such as when after praying for divine guidance, "nearly all the bishops approve an unwarranted invasion, like that of Afghanistan", or when the Bishop of Manchester advocates a regime of moral and physical discipline so that the English would be prepared in warfare, like hunting dogs attached to a fox, to "die biting".[73] Evidence of the superior moral status of those belonging to non-European races and non-Christian religions was also grist to Spencer's mill, severing the link between Christianity and moral superiority. So, having listed examples from travellers' accounts of hospitable and generous Australians, New Zealanders, Iroquois and Africans, Spencer concluded that the name "savages" was misleading and that it might "with greater propriety be applied to many among ourselves and our European neighbours"; and that supposedly Christian virtues "may be shown in a higher degree" where they have never been preached than in countries where "they are ostentatiously professed and perpetually enjoined".[74]

In the final volume of the *Principles of Sociology*, Spencer even managed to find a way of attacking optimism, socialism, British imperialism, militarism, and Christianity all in one breath. His point was that sentimental socialism relied on an unduly optimistic estimate of the current state of human nature and the altruism of which people were currently capable. People only needed to look around them, he said, to recognise that they were living in a world not only populated, but led, by selfish and barbarous people. He then offered as examples the policy of "unscrupulous aggrandizement" pursued by the British government, the conquests being made "from base and selfish motives alone", and the violent appropriations that resulted from quarrels with native peoples. His summary of British imperial policy was brutally short: "First men are sent to teach the heathens Christianity, and then Christians are sent to mow them down with machine-guns! ... The policy is simple and uniform – bibles first, bomb-shells after". Spencer went on to cite the terrifying rate of homicides in the United States, which had risen from 12 per day to 30 per day; and the corruption that was rife in America both among the police forces and businessmen. Now, given all this evidence of the continued selfishness and brutality of humanity in the 1890s, Spencer asked sarcastically, did the socialists seriously believe they could construct a society "pervaded by the sentiment of brotherhood" in which "regard for others is supreme?"[75]

Regardless of Spencer's dissent from the burgeoning socialist, co-operative and communist movements of the 1880s and 1890s, and despite the modifications in his own terminology, the term "altruism" continued to be associated with views more akin to his earlier evolutionary optimism. One of the most widely read books about altruism of the 1890s was the Scottish evangelical writer Henry Drummond's hugely popular *Ascent of Man* (1894). Drummond's work was based, at least in part, on Spencer's analysis, as presented in the *Data of Ethics*. Drummond wrote passionately about the importance of altruism as a factor in evolution, from the "self-sacrifice" of the lowest single-celled organism in its act of "protoplasmic fission2, to the devotion of a mother to her children. The evolution of life was described as a "love story" in which altruism was present from the outset as the driving force in the "struggle for the life of others".[76] This popularised and Christianised form of 1870s Spencerian science provoked Spencer's friend, the journalist and Darwinian, Eliza Lynn Linton[77], to launch a furious assault on Drummond, in the pages of the *Fortnightly Review* in September 1894, accusing him simultaneously of "simple and direct plagiarism" and of reducing Spencer's views to the level of "unscientific nonsense". Compare Spencer's *Data of Ethics* with the *Ascent of Man*, Lynn Linton said, and you will see the difference between "the real scientific thinker" and "the pseudo-scientist writing clap-trap for an ignorant public".[78] The article had, in fact, been commissioned by Spencer himself, who had written to his friend saying that someone should write a reply but that he would not like to undertake it himself and that "looking around for a proxy I thought of you". Spencer was delighted with the result and applauded her denunciation not only of Drummond, but of "the public taste which swallows with greediness these semi-scientific sentimentalities".[79]

Whether it was at Spencer's specific behest or on Eliza Lynn Linton's own initiative, the article damning Drummond for plagiarism also contained the statement that even great thinkers such as Darwin and Spencer had predecessors whom they had to acknowledge. As a result, Lynn Linton went on, "Descartes and Lamarck, Proudhon and Comte, are not without honour in the new temples raised to Truth and Science".[80] Even in 1894, nearly fifty years after Comte's death, it was hard to get away from his name, and from the question of Herbert Spencer's relationship with his work, when writing about altruism.

Anti-Aggression, Altruism and Politics

Whether advocating sternness at home or kindness abroad, Spencer's writings on the philosophy and science of altruism had the virtue of speaking to the concerns of his readers: concerns about everyday life, about domestic politics, about Christian religion, and about international affairs. We find in his writings evidence that, as with discussions of altruism to this day, the fundamental questions the topic raised were not just about evolutionary theory or the logical connections between science and ethics, but included political ones about the boundaries of moral communities; about the mechanisms of social progress; and about relationships between the individual and the collective, between the nations of the world, and between religion and ethics.

Like many other unbelievers of the period, especially the positivists, Spencer was engaged in a process of moralising unbelief. This was one of the ways in which the discourse of altruism was so helpful: it represented the creation of an autonomous, scientific moral thought-world, independent of the language and doctrines of the churches, which could be used to take the moral high ground. Just as Spencer's passionate pacifism, or "anti-aggression" as he called it (he even founded an Anti-Aggression League in 1882[81]), was one of the uniting threads throughout his ethical writings, it was also something which, unlike most other matters, united him, on the moral high ground, with the positivists. In an address delivered at the positivist commemoration of new year's day in 1880, on the subject of "Empire and Humanity", for example, Frederic Harrison had denounced the British empire, in terms that would have warmed Spencer's heart, as one of "conquest and domination", waging unjust wars against the Zulu people, and against the Afghan races. "We who look forward to a purely human religion", Harrison said, "can hope but little from the Churches in dealing with this Central Asian crime". He expressed dismay, like Spencer's, at the collusion of the established faiths in the crimes of temporal authorities. Christianity, Harrison said, was complicit in imperialist aggression and commercial exploitation.[82] Divided over the question of Spencer's dependence or lack of it on Comte's philosophy, Harrison and Spencer were united in their condemnation of the British government's treatment of foreign nations and their belief in the moral inferiority of Christianity.

Spencer's callous suggestion, with which we started, that we should calculate someone's moral and social value before helping them is one that does not endear him to many modern readers.

However there may still be a place for the voice of Herbert Spencer in contemporary discussions. His eloquent assaults on those Christian leaders who profess devotion to a religion whose founder told them to turn the other cheek, and who yet adopt the militaristic policy of striking their enemy lest they should be struck; and his indignation at the abuse of military and economic might to make selfish gains at the expense of other nations are both aspects of his philosophy that certainly still sound relevant today. The following report, for instance, carried in the *Washington Times* in September 2003, encapsulates just the sort of contradiction that Spencer described as arising from the simultaneous adherence to an uncivilised religion of enmity and a purported religion of amity:

> FORT STEWART, Ga. – President Bush yesterday rallied U.S. troops for the continuing war against terror, earning a resounding "hoo-ah" from 15,000 camo-clad soldiers, a day after leading the nation in a somber remembrance of the September 11 terrorist attack victims.[83]

The day after the second anniversary of the terrorist attacks on New York and Washington, the devoutly Christian Mr Bush said: "In this new kind of war, America has followed a new strategy. We are not waiting for further attacks on our citizens. We are striking our enemies before they can strike us again."[84] A contemporary sympathiser with Herbert Spencer, who believed that the demands of altruism, at home and abroad, had to be balanced against the fundamental ethical principle that each individual had an equal right to freedom; and who condemned counter-productive and expensive governmental interference as much in injustices abroad as in inequalities closer to home, would have stern words to say, no doubt, about George W. Bush's 87-billion-dollar crusade against those he terms "the enemies of freedom" and about his assertion that this aggression will bring "justice" to those who plot against America.[85] Spencer's remaining hope, in 1896, had been that as the evolutionary process of integration was increasingly effective, not only within each society, but globally, an international authority would be set up over all nations which might, "by forbidding wars between any of its constituent nations, put an end to the rebarbarization which is continually undoing civilization".[86]   If only it were that simple.

On 11 September in New York, in the year 1879, the new edition of the weekly journal *The Nation* came out. It contained an unsigned article on Herbert Spencer's recently published *Data of Ethics*, pronouncing it "the most noteworthy production of its energetic author".[87]   The author was an assistant professor of physiology at Harvard with an interest in evolution, psychology and philosophy – namely William James.   The article was scathing about Spencer's attempt to apply evolution to absolutely everything, including moral philosophy, and predicted that, when the intellectual furore surrounding evolution had died down, philosophical discussions about the fundamental reasons for action would continue much as they had before.   James somewhat sarcastically went on to describe Spencer's imagined ideal future state, in which all shall act out of a spontaneous and unconscious desire to increase the total amount of vitality on the earth; unconscious of their motive, that is, unless "perchance the theory as well as the practice of evolution shall have become ingrained into the nervous system of us all".[88]   James also expressed scepticism about the possibility of persuading anyone, who happened not to be constituted in a way that was conducive to this altruistic direction of social evolution, to change their behaviour accordingly.   Finally, the review noted that whereas in Germany the "struggle for existence" had been invoked by those defending "the most cynical assertions of brute egoism", Mr Spencer had used the same scientific theories to argue for "an almost Quakerish humanitarianism and regard for peace".[89] "Frequently in these pages," James noticed, "does his indignation at the ruling powers of Britain burst forth, for their policy of conquest over lower races".[90]   But given the inability of the evolutionary ethicist to predict exactly which policies would prove most successful in fostering sympathy, peace and justice, even if all people were constituted to pursue those aims, many difficult questions still remained, James concluded, questions such as when we might expect an equitable and peaceful world to arrive and exactly how to bring it about.   "What kind of fellows shall we be willing to be peaceful with, and whose sympathy shall we enjoy?" James asked, "Shall we settle down to peaceful competition with the Chinese? Shall our mess-mates in the millennial equilibrium be of the fat-minded Esquimaux type?"[91]

Thus James' response to Spencer's pacifist manifesto of 1879, along with Spencer's own work, identified the key political questions that systems of evolutionary ethics can raise but never definitively answer. To whom, precisely, in our own society rather than an ideal one, do we owe altruism, and to what extent? Should we deal with all individuals and all nations equally or is it right that there should be some sort of hierarchy of altruism? Should the individual or the state administer that altruism? Through what individual or collective measures can society be made more altruistic? How can we achieve this while still aspiring to protect the freedom of each and to provide justice for all? And how can professions of Christianity be combined with a militaristic and vengeful foreign policy without hypocrisy? Although we will not today approve of all of Herbert Spencer's answers, nor Auguste Comte's, nor William James', we should still attend to their questions.[92]

Acknowledgements

For institutional and financial support for the research from which this paper arises, I am grateful to the British Academy for a Postdoctoral Research Fellowship, to Churchill College, Cambridge for a Junior Research Fellowship, and to the Cambridge Faculty of Divinity. I am very grateful to Greta Jones for inviting me to participate in the Galton Institute Symposium and to Betty Nixon for her efficient administration both of the event and of the production of this book. For valuable suggestions regarding the content of this paper I am indebted to Emily Butterworth and, especially, to Jim Moore, whose own work on evolution, politics and Victorian religion has been a source of particular illumination.

Notes

[1] James R. Moore, "Herbert Spencer's Henchmen: The Evolution of Protestant Liberals in Late Nineteenth-Century America," in *Darwinism*

and Divinity: Essays on Evolution and Religious Belief, ed. John R. Durant (Oxford: Blackwell, 1985), p. 79.

2 On the potentially misleading nature of the label '*laissez-faire*' as applied to Spencer and other nineteenth-century political economists, see Mark Francis, "Herbert Spencer and the Myth of Laissez-Faire," *Journal of the History of Ideas* 39 (1978): 317-328.

3 The most significant exception to this rule, of course, being J. D. Y. Peel's outstanding study of the social and intellectual sources and contexts of Spencer's sociology. J. D. Y. Peel, *Herbert Spencer: The Evolution of a Sociologist* (London: Heinemann, 1971). On Spencer's reception by contemporaries and by posterity, see pp. 1-6.

4 James Moore's critique of Ruse's evolutionary ethics, for example, deployed this strategy. James R. Moore, "Born-Again Social Darwinism," *Annals of Science* 44 (1987): 409-417.

5 See Lawrence G. Miller, "Fated Genes," in *The Sociobiology Debate: Readings on the Ethical and Scientific Issues Concerning Sociobiology*, ed. Arthur L. Caplan (New York: Harper and Row, 1978), pp. 269-279; Sociobiology Study Group of Science for the People, "Sociobiology - Another Biological Determinism," in *The Sociobiology Debate: Readings on the Ethical and Scientific Issues Concerning Sociobiology*, ed. Arthur L. Caplan (New York: Harper and Row, 1978), pp. 280-290. Miller argues that Spencer and Wilson were both guilty of offering 'the false certainty of evolutionary positivism', p. 278.

6 Edward O. Wilson, *Sociobiology: The New Synthesis* (Cambridge, MA: Harvard University Press, 1975), p. 3.

7 Richard Dawkins, *The Selfish Gene*, new ed. (Oxford: Oxford University Press, 1989), p. 3.

8 Daniel C. Dennett, *Darwin's Dangerous Idea: Evolution and the Meanings of Life* (London: Penguin, 1996); Robert Richards, *Darwin and the Emergence of Evolutionary Theories of Mind and Behavior* (Chicago: University of Chicago Press, 1987); Michael Ruse, *Evolutionary Naturalism: Selected Essays* (London and New York: Routledge, 1995).

9 On some of the other differences between the various recent defenders of evolutionary ethics see Peter G. Woolcock, "The Case against Evolutionary Ethics Today," in *Biology and the Foundation of Ethics*, ed. Jane Maienschein and Michael Ruse (Cambridge: Cambridge University Press, 1999), pp. 276-306.

10 Dennett, *Darwin's Dangerous Idea: Evolution and the Meanings of Life,* esp. pp. 393-7, 461-6, 477.

11 Steven Pinker, *The Blank Slate: The Modern Denial of Human Nature* (London: Allen Lane, 2002), pp. 15-16, 150. Pinker accuses Spencer both of heinous Social Darwinism, or 'Social Spencerism' as he suggests it should be renamed, and of committing the 'naturalistic fallacy.'

12 Michael Ruse, "A Darwinian Naturalist's Perspective on Altruism," in *Altruism and Altruistic Love: Science, Philosophy, and Religion in Dialogue*, ed. Stephen G. Post, et al. (Oxford: Oxford University Press, 2002), pp. 151-167, especially p. 162.

13 Michael Ruse, "Evolutionary Ethics in the Twentieth Century: Julian Sorell Huxley and George Gaylord Simpson," in *Biology and the Foundation of Ethics*, ed. Jane Maienschein and Michael Ruse (Cambridge: Cambridge University Press, 1999), p. 199.

14 Richards, *Darwin and the Emergence of Evolutionary Theories of Mind and Behavior* pp. 595-627.

15 *Ibid.*, pp. 295-330, quotation p. 330.

16 One example of an interesting parallel between Darwin and Spencer on this question is Spencer's account of how 'survival of the fittest among tribes' would originally have given rise to cooperative and altruistic behaviour. Herbert Spencer, *Principles of Ethics*, 2 vols. (London: Williams and Norgate, 1892-3), vol. 1, p. 314.

17 *Ibid.*, vol. 2, p. 358.

18 James R. Moore, "Speaking of "Science and Religion" - Then and Now," *History of Science* 30 (1992), p. 314.

19 For a fuller treatment of the significance of the introduction of the language of altruism, see Thomas Dixon, "The Invention of Altruism: Auguste Comte's *Positive Polity* and Respectable Unbelief in Victorian Britain," in *Science and Beliefs: From Natural Philosophy to Natural Science*, ed. David Knight and Matthew Eddy (Aldershot: Ashgate, in press).

20 Spencer for many years denied that he knew the phrase 'social statics' had been used by anyone other than himself when he wrote his first book, of that title, in 1851, let alone that it was a Comtean coinage. Eventually, however, an 1891 footnote to one of his reprinted essays, Spencer admitted that he must have got the idea of dividing social science into 'statics' and 'dynamics' from John Stuart Mill's *Logic*, which, although not naming Comte, had taken the distinction from

him. Herbert Spencer, "Reasons for Dissenting from the Philosophy of M. Comte," in *Essays: Scientific, Political, and Speculative* (London: Williams and Norgate, 1891), , p. 134n.

[21] For a discussion of the recurrent connections made between Spencer and Comte and an analysis of the extent of the dependence, if any, see Sydney Eisen, "Herbert Spencer and the Spectre of Comte," *Journal of British Studies* 7 (1967): 48-67.

[22] Spencer recounts, in his autobiography, an episode in which he went to great lengths, in 1889, to track down some newspaper articles he had written nearly fifty years earlier, to prove that he had not used the term 'sociology' in them, which would have indicated that, contrary to his constant claims to the contrary, he had indeed read Comte prior to the composition of the *Social Statics*. Herbert Spencer, *An Autobiography*, 2 vols. (London: Williams and Norgate, 1904), vol. 1, pp. 255f.

[23] [G. H. Lewes], "Contemporary Literature of France," *Westminster Review* 58, n.s. 2 (1852), pp. 617-8.

[24] See Stefan Collini, *Public Moralists: Political Thought and Intellectual Life in Britain 1850-1930* (Oxford: Clarendon Press, 1991), pp. 60-90; Dixon, "The Invention of Altruism: Auguste Comte's *Positive Polity* and Respectable Unbelief in Victorian Britain".

[25] Thomas H. Huxley, "On the Physical Basis of Life," in *Lay Sermons, Essays, and Reviews* (London: Macmillan, 1893), p. 121.

[26] On the Religion of Humanity and its British adherents, see John Hedley Brooke and Geoffrey Cantor, *Reconstructing Nature: The Engagement of Science and Religion* (Edinburgh: T. and T. Clark, 1998), pp. 47-57; Auguste Comte, *The Catechism of Positive Religion*, trans. Richard Congreve, 3rd ed. (London: Kegan Paul, Trench, Trübner and Co., 1891); Terence R. Wright, *The Religion of Humanity: The Impact of Comtean Positivism on Victorian Britain* (Cambridge: Cambridge University Press, 1986).

[27] Mary Booth, *Charles Booth: A Memoir* (London: Macmillan, 1918), pp. 8-9; Dixon, "The Invention of Altruism: Auguste Comte's *Positive Polity* and Respectable Unbelief in Victorian Britain,"; J. B. Schneewind, *Sidgwick's Ethics and Victorian Moral Philosophy* (Oxford: Clarendon Press, 1977), p. 42; Beatrice Webb, *My Apprenticeship* (London: Longmans, Green and Co., 1926), p. 149.

[28] Herbert Spencer, *Principles of Psychology*, 2nd ed., 2 vols. (London: Williams and Norgate, 1870-2), vol. 2, p. 607n.

29 F. W. Farrar, *The Witness of Christ to History, Being the Hulsean Lectures for the Year 1870* (London and New York: Macmillan, 1871), pp. 144-6.

30 Herbert Spencer, *The Study of Sociology* (London: King, 1873), p. 182.

31 James McCosh, "Herbert Spencer's Data of Ethics," *Princeton Review* 4 n.s. (1879), p. 627.

32 Henry Sidgwick, "Mr Spencer's Ethical System," *Mind* 5 (1880), p. 221.

33 Given the association between 'altruism' and Comte made by Spencer and by his reviewers during the 1870s, I would not go so far as Stefan Collini, who suggests that by the mid-1870s, the word 'no longer needed to carry its identity papers with it'. The Comtist association lasted, for some, into the 1880s and 1890s. Despite this, Collini is essentially right that the Comtist association faded as the term came into wider use, and that the success of Spencer's work was certainly instrumental in that process. Collini, *Public Moralists: Political Thought and Intellectual Life in Britain 1850-1930*, p. 61.

34 On Spencer's role in the popularisation in America of his secularised 'theodicy' in which the evolution of perfect society in future could justify the natural evils of the present, see Moore, "Herbert Spencer's Henchmen: The Evolution of Protestant Liberals in Late Nineteenth-Century America".

35 The phrase is one of George Eliot's, used in 1856 as part of a sarcastic critique of some of the more sentimental aspects of Dickens' novels. [George Eliot], "The Natural History of German Life," *Westminster Review* 66, n.s. 10 (1856), p. 55.

36 For Comte's vision of society, see Auguste Comte, *System of Positive Polity, or Treatise on Sociology, Instituting the Religion of Humanity*, trans. Edward Spencer Beesly, et al., 4 vols. (London: Longman's, Green and Co., 1875-1877); John Stuart Mill, *Auguste Comte and Positivism* (London: Trübner, 1865).

37 Spencer, *An Autobiography*, pp. 445-446.

38 Spencer, *Principles of Psychology*, vol. 2, pp. 578-591.

39 *Ibid.*, pp. 592-606, quotation from p. 603.

40 *Ibid.*, pp. 607-626, quotations from pp. 609, 614.

41 *Ibid.*, pp. 612-613.

42 *Ibid.*, pp. 618-619.

[43] Comte, *System of Positive Polity, or Treatise on Sociology, Instituting the Religion of Humanity,* especially vol. 1, pp. 456-594.

[44] Spencer, *Principles of Psychology,* p. 622.

[45] Charles Darwin, *The Descent of Man, and Selection in Relation to Sex,* 2 vols. (London: Murray, 1871); Charles Darwin, *The Expression of the Emotions in Man and Animals* (London: Murray, 1872); Thomas Dixon, *From Passions to Emotions: The Creation of a Secular Psychological Category* (Cambridge: Cambridge University Press, 2003), pp. 159-179; Richards, *Darwin and the Emergence of Evolutionary Theories of Mind and Behavior,* pp. 185-242; Robert Richards, "Darwin's Romantic Biology: The Foundation of His Evolutionary Ethics," in *Biology and the Foundation of Ethics,* ed. Jane Maienschein and Michael Ruse (Cambridge: Cambridge University Press, 1999), pp. 113-153; Robert Richards, "Darwin on Mind, Morals and Emotions," in *The Cambridge Companion to Darwin,* ed. Jonathan Hodge and Gregory Radick (Cambridge: Cambridge University Press, 2003), pp. 92-115.

[46] Richards, *Darwin and the Emergence of Evolutionary Theories of Mind and Behavior,* pp. 295-330.

[47] Two useful recent books covering much of the recent conceptual and theoretical issues, such as the dispute over the viability of group-selection as an evolutionary mechanism, as well as various philosophical and theological implications, see Stephen G. Post et al., eds., *Altruism and Altruistic Love: Science, Philosophy and Religion in Dialogue* (Oxford and New York: Oxford University Press, 2002); Elliott Sober and David Sloan Wilson, *Unto Others: The Evolution and Psychology of Unselfish Behavior* (Cambridge, MA and London: Harvard University Press, 1998).

[48] The bad-tempered but entertaining exchange between Dawkins and Mary Midgley arose from just this confusion. Richard Dawkins, *The Selfish Gene* (Oxford: Oxford University Press, 1976); Richard Dawkins, "In Defence of Selfish Genes," *Philosohpy* 56 (1981): 556-573; Mary Midgley, "Gene-Juggling," *Philosohpy* 54 (1979): 439-458.

[49] Herbert Spencer, *The Data of Ethics* (London: Williams and Norgate, 1879), p. 201.

[50] *Ibid.,* p. 203.

[51] McCosh, "Herbert Spencer's Data of Ethics,", p. 627.

[52] Alfred W. Benn, "Another View of Mr Spencer's Ethics," *Mind* 5 (1880), p. 509.

[53] Spencer, *The Data of Ethics*, p. 210.

[54] *Ibid.*, pp. 210-211.

[55] See Herbert Spencer, *Education: Intellectual, Moral, and Physical* (London: Manwaring, 1861).

[56] Spencer, *The Data of Ethics*, p. 218.

[57] *Ibid.*, p. 240.

[58] *Ibid.*, p. 257.

[59] Quoted in Sydney Ross, "Scientist: The Story of a Word," *Annals of Science* 18, no. 2 (1962), p. 77. I am grateful to Jim Moore for drawing my attention to this article by Ross and to the Allen quotation.

[60] Spencer, *An Autobiography*, pp. 445-446.

[61] Frederic Harrison, "The Ghost of Religion," *Nineteenth Century* 15 (1884), p. 496; Herbert Spencer, "Religion: A Retrospect and Prospect," *Nineteenth Century* 15 (1884), p. 12.

[62] "Mr Herbert Spencer and the Comtists," *The Times*, 9, 12, 15 September, 1884.

[63] W. Boyd Carpenter, *Christian Altruism: A Sermon Preached in the Private Chapel, Windsor Castle, Sunday 1 April, 1883* (Printed by the Queen's Command, 1883).

[64] Anon., "The Extravagance of Altruism," *Spectator* 68 (1892), p. 671.

[65] Anon., "The Weak Point in Altruism," *Spectator* 79 (1897), p. 516.

[66] Robert Blatchford, *Altruism: Christ's Glorious Gospel of Love against Man's Dismal Science of Greed (Clarion Pamphlet No. 22)* (London: Clarion Press, 1898), p. 3.

[67] Spencer, *Principles of Ethics*, vol. 2, p. 268.

[68] *Ibid.*, vol. 2, pp. 270-272.

[69] *Ibid.*, vol. 1, p. vi.

[70] *Ibid.*, vol. 2, p. 392.

[71] *Ibid.*, vol. 2, p. 394.

[72] *Ibid.*, p. v.

[73] *Ibid.*, vol. 1, pp. 316-317.

[74] *Ibid.*, vol. 1, pp. 384, 399.

[75] Herbert Spencer, *The Principles of Sociology*, 3 vols., vol. 3 (London: Williams and Norgate, 1896), pp. 574-575.

[76] Henry Drummond, *The Lowell Lectures on the Ascent of Man* (London: Hodder and Stoughton, 1899), pp. 275-341.

[77] On Linton's opposition to the exclusion by Thomas Huxley of women from the Ethnological Society, see Evelleen Richards, "Huxley and Woman's Place in Science: The 'Woman Question' and the Control of Victorian Anthropology," in *History, Humanity and Evolution: Essays for John C. Greene*, ed. James R. Moore (Cambridge: Cambridge University Press, 1989), pp. 253-284.

[78] E. Lynn Linton, "Professor Henry Drummond's Discovery," *Fortnightly Review* 56 n.s. (1894), pp. 453-454.

[79] David Duncan, *The Life and Letters of Herbert Spencer* (London: Methuen, 1908), p. 363.

[80] Linton, "Professor Henry Drummond's Discovery," p. 448.

[81] Duncan, *The Life and Letters of Herbert Spencer,* pp. 221-224.

[82] Frederic Harrison, "Empire and Humanity," *Fortnightly Review* 27 n.s. (1880), quotations from pp. 292-294.

[83] *Washington Times* online: http://www.washtimes.com, consulted 15 September 2003.

[84] White House official website: http://www.politicsol.com/govsites/white-house.html, consulted 15 September 2003.

[85] *Ibid.*

[86] Spencer, *Principles of Sociology*, vol. 3, p. 600.

[87] [William James], "Herbert Spencer's Data of Ethics," *The Nation* 29 (1879): 178-179.

[88] *Ibid.*, p. 179.

[89] Spencer's father, George, had indeed been a Quaker. Peel, *Herbert Spencer: The Evolution of a Sociologist*, p. 8.

[90] [James], "Herbert Spencer's Data of Ethics,", p. 179.

[91] *Ibid.*

[92] For an examination of how Ruse's more recent evolutionary ethics raises these sorts of political and religious questions, see Moore, "Born-Again Social Darwinism".

Bibliography

Anon. "The Extravagance of Altruism." *Spectator* 68 (1892): 671-672.
————. "The Weak Point in Altruism." *Spectator* 79 (1897): 515-516.
Benn, Alfred W. "Another View of Mr Spencer's Ethics." *Mind* 5 (1880): 489-512.

Blatchford, Robert. *Altruism: Christ's Glorious Gospel of Love against Man's Dismal Science of Greed (Clarion Pamphlet No. 22).* London: Clarion Press, 1898.

Booth, Mary. *Charles Booth: A Memoir.* London: Macmillan, 1918.

Brooke, John Hedley, and Geoffrey Cantor. *Reconstructing Nature: The Engagement of Science and Religion.* Edinburgh: T. and T. Clark, 1998.

Carpenter, W. Boyd. *Christian Altruism: A Sermon Preached in the Private Chapel, Windsor Castle, Sunday 1 April, 1883:* Printed by the Queen's Command, 1883.

Collini, Stefan. *Public Moralists: Political Thought and Intellectual Life in Britain 1850-1930.* Oxford: Clarendon Press, 1991.

Comte, Auguste. *System of Positive Polity, or Treatise on Sociology, Instituting the Religion of Humanity.* Translated by Edward Spencer Beesly, J. H. Bridges, Richard Congreve, Frederic Harrison, Fanny Hertz, Henry Dix Hutton, Samuel Lobb, Godfrey Lushington and Vernon Lushington. 4 vols. London: Longman's, Green and Co., 1875-1877.

———. *The Catechism of Positive Religion.* Translated by Richard Congreve. 3rd ed. London: Kegan Paul, Trench, Trübner and Co., 1891.

Darwin, Charles. *The Descent of Man, and Selection in Relation to Sex.* 2 vols. London: Murray, 1871.

———. *The Expression of the Emotions in Man and Animals.* London: Murray, 1872.

Dawkins, Richard. *The Selfish Gene.* Oxford: Oxford University Press, 1976.

———. "In Defence of Selfish Genes." *Philosophy* 56 (1981): 556-573.

———. *The Selfish Gene.* new ed. Oxford: Oxford University Press, 1989.

Dennett, Daniel C. *Darwin's Dangerous Idea: Evolution and the Meanings of Life.* London: Penguin, 1996.

Dixon, Thomas. *From Passions to Emotions: The Creation of a Secular Psychological Category.* Cambridge: Cambridge University Press, 2003.

———. "The Invention of Altruism: Auguste Comte's *Positive Polity* and Respectable Unbelief in Victorian Britain." In *Science and Beliefs: From Natural Philosophy to Natural Science*, edited by David Knight and Matthew Eddy. Aldershot: Ashgate, in press.

Drummond, Henry. *The Lowell Lectures on the Ascent of Man.* London: Hodder and Stoughton, 1899.

Duncan, David. *The Life and Letters of Herbert Spencer*. London: Methuen, 1908.

Eisen, Sydney. "Herbert Spencer and the Spectre of Comte." *Journal of British Studies* 7 (1967): 48-67.

[Eliot, George]. "The Natural History of German Life." *Westminster Review* 66, n.s. 10 (1856): 51-79.

Farrar, F.W. *The Witness of Christ to History, Being the Hulsean Lectures for the Year 1870*. London and New York: Macmillan, 1871.

Francis, Mark. "Herbert Spencer and the Myth of Laissez-Faire." *Journal of the History of Ideas* 39 (1978): 317-328.

Harrison, Frederic. "Empire and Humanity." *Fortnightly Review* 27 n.s. (1880): 288-208.

———. "The Ghost of Religion." *Nineteenth Century* 15 (1884): 494-506.

———. "Mr Herbert Spencer and the Comtists." *The Times*, 12 September,1884, p. 8.

Huxley, Thomas H. "On the Physical Basis of Life." In *Lay Sermons, Essays, and Reviews*. London: Macmillan, 1893, pp. 104-127.

[James, William]. "Herbert Spencer's Data of Ethics." *The Nation* 29 (1879): 178-179.

[Lewes, G. H.]. "Contemporary Literature of France." *Westminster Review* 58, n.s. 2 (1852): 614-630.

Linton, E. Lynn. "Professor Henry Drummond's Discovery." *Fortnightly Review* 56 n.s. (1894): 448-457.

McCosh, James. "Herbert Spencer's Data of Ethics." *Princeton Review* 4 n.s. (1879): 607-636.

Midgley, Mary. "Gene-Juggling." *Philosophy* 54 (1979): 439-458.

Mill, John Stuart. *Auguste Comte and Positivism*. London: Trübner, 1865.

Miller, Lawrence G. "Fated Genes." In *The Sociobiology Debate: Readings on the Ethical and Scientific Issues Concerning Sociobiology*, edited by Arthur L. Caplan. New York: Harper and Row, 1978, pp. 269-279

Moore, James R. "Herbert Spencer's Henchmen: The Evolution of Protestant Liberals in Late Nineteenth-Century America." In *Darwinism and Divinity: Essays on Evolution and Religious Belief*, edited by John R. Durant. Oxford: Blackwell, 1985, pp. 76-100

———. "Born-Again Social Darwinism." *Annals of Science* 44 (1987): 409-417.

————. "Speaking of "Science and Religion" - Then and Now." *History of Science* 30 (1992): 311-323.

Peel, J. D. Y. *Herbert Spencer: The Evolution of a Sociologist.* London: Heinemann, 1971.

Pinker, Steven, *The Blank Slate: The Modern Denial of Human Nature.* London: Allen Lane, 2002.

Post, Stephen G., Lynn G. Underwood, Jeffrey P. Schloss, and William B. Hurlbut, eds. *Altruism and Altruistic Love: Science, Philosophy and Religion in Dialogue.* Oxford and New York: Oxford University Press, 2002.

Richards, Evelleen. "Huxley and Woman's Place in Science: The 'Woman Question' and the Control of Victorian Anthropology." In *History, Humanity and Evolution: Essays for John C. Greene*, edited by James R. Moore. Cambridge: Cambridge University Press, 1989, pp. 253-284

Richards, Robert. *Darwin and the Emergence of Evolutionary Theories of Mind and Behavior.* Chicago: University of Chicago Press, 1987.

————. "Darwin's Romantic Biology: The Foundation of His Evolutionary Ethics." In *Biology and the Foundation of Ethics*, edited by Jane Maienschein and Michael Ruse. Cambridge: Cambridge University Press, 1999, pp. 113-153

————. "Darwin on Mind, Morals and Emotions." In *The Cambridge Companion to Darwin*, edited by Jonathan Hodge and Gregory Radick. Cambridge: Cambridge University Press, 2003, pp. 92-115

Ross, Sydney. "Scientist: The Story of a Word." *Annals of Science* 18, no. 2 (1962): 65-85.

Ruse, Michael. *Evolutionary Naturalism: Selected Essays.* London and New York: Routledge, 1995.

————. "Evolutionary Ethics in the Twentieth Century: Julian Sorell Huxley and George Gaylord Simpson." In *Biology and the Foundation of Ethics*, edited by Jane Maienschein and Michael Ruse. Cambridge: Cambridge University Press, 1999, pp. 198-224

————. "A Darwinian Naturalist's Perspective on Altruism." In *Altruism and Altruistic Love: Science, Philosophy, and Religion in Dialogue*, edited by Stephen G. Post, Lynn G. Underwood, Jeffrey P. Schloss and William B. Hurlbut. Oxford: Oxford University Press, 2002, pp. 151-167

Schneewind, J. B. *Sidgwick's Ethics and Victorian Moral Philosophy.* Oxford: Clarendon Press, 1977.

Sidgwick, Henry. "Mr Spencer's Ethical System." *Mind* 5 (1880): 216-226.

Sober, Elliott, and David Sloan Wilson. *Unto Others: The Evolution and Psychology of Unselfish Behavior.* Cambridge, MA and London: Harvard University Press, 1998.

Sociobiology Study Group of Science for the People. "Sociobiology - Another Biological Determinism." In *The Sociobiology Debate: Readings on the Ethical and Scientific Issues Concerning Sociobiology,* edited by Arthur L. Caplan. New York: Harper and Row, 1978, pp. 280-290

Spencer, Herbert. *Education: Intellectual, Moral, and Physical.* London: Manwaring, 1861.

———. *Principles of Psychology.* 2nd ed. 2 vols. London: Williams and Norgate, 1870-2.

———. *The Study of Sociology.* London: King, 1873.

———. *The Data of Ethics.* London: Williams and Norgate, 1879.

———. "Religion: A Retrospect and Prospect." *Nineteenth Century* 15 (1884): 1-12.

———. "Mr Herbert Spencer and the Comtists." *The Times,* 9 September,1884, p. 5.

———. "Mr Herbert Spencer and the Comtists." *The Times,* 15 September,1884, p. 7.

———. "Reasons for Dissenting from the Philosophy of M. Comte." In *Essays: Scientific, Political, and Speculative.* London: Williams and Norgate, 1891, pp. 118-144

———. *Principles of Ethics.* 2 vols. London: Williams and Norgate, 1892-3.

———. *The Principles of Sociology.* 3 vols. Vol. 3. London: Williams and Norgate, 1896.

———. *An Autobiography.* 2 vols. London: Williams and Norgate, 1904.

Webb, Beatrice. *My Apprenticeship.* London: Longmans, Green and Co., 1926.

Wilson, Edward O. *Sociobiology: The New Synthesis.* Cambridge, MA: Harvard University Press, 1975.

Woolcock, Peter G. "The Case against Evolutionary Ethics Today." In *Biology and the Foundation of Ethics,* edited by Jane Maienschein and Michael Ruse. Cambridge: Cambridge University Press, 1999, pp. 276-306

Wright, Terence R. *The Religion of Humanity: The Impact of Comtean Positivism on Victorian Britain.* Cambridge: Cambridge University Press, 1986.

6. Galton Lecture 2003: Spencer In History: The Second Century

J.D.Y. Peel

1.

About the first week in November, for most of the last thirty years, I have given a lecture on Herbert Spencer to a first-year class of sociology or anthropology students. It has usually come in a course on Social Theory that starts with the Enlightenment and takes them up to about the late 1960s. Such a course can be organised around theoretical approaches – functionalism, structuralism, phenomenology, social exchange and so on – or historically, in terms of a narrative that shows the intellectual filiation of our current concerns, and at the same time the links between particular theorists and the contexts in which they wrote. My own preference has always been for the latter approach. Yet it has to be more than intellectual history, since the aim is to introduce the students to social theory through a reading of a sequence of key texts – works such as the first two chapters of *The Wealth of Nations*, sections of Marx's *The German Ideology* or Simmel's essay on "The Stranger". For Spencer I use those clear, vigorous essays in which he first set out his theory of social evolution: "Progress: its Law and Cause" (1857) and "The Social Organism" (1860). Underlying these choices is a fundamental question, which forces itself on us as we commemorate the centenary of Spencer's death: why and how should we remember our intellectual forbears, the "founding fathers" of the disciplines we practice?

Remembering is a temporary closing of the gap between past and present. We attempt it in two opposite ways: by bringing the past to us, or by visiting the past ourselves. Let us call these presentist and historicist strategies. With the first, we bring the intellectual past to us by reading its texts as if they were meant for us to read in our present situation – if not always as vehicles of timeless wisdom, then at least as works which grappled in an

125

exemplary way with problems that are still our problems. These qualities are what makes us call them "classics". The other strategy is to historicize, by placing these same texts in their other, original context, so that (having been imaginatively taken there) we are in the end brought to know how far we have travelled from it; and at the same time to appreciate the pioneers who started the journey for us.

On the whole, we tend to be presentist about art, literature and philosophy, believing that these things address perennial human problems and aspirations.   On the other, even the greatest achievements of past science are regarded as out of date; or rather it is enough that they are present as the hidden foundations of the modern knowledge that has been erected on top of them. Natural scientists leave past science for the historians of science. My eldest son did a PhD in plant genetics[1], but never read a word of Galton or Mendel; and I'm sure that the main function of his copy of *The Origin of Species* is to look good on his bookshelf. But the social sciences, saturated as they are with human value and philosophical ambiguity, straddle the divide, and require a measure both of presentist and historicist treatment.   Spencer, of course, is especially problematic, since his extraordinary *oeuvre* stretched from ethics to biology. So there are two main questions we need to ask of him: What, if anything, is worth reading in Spencer now? Have we given Spencer his due place in the history of thought, and in our own intellectual descent?

In formulating our relationship to the past, we are prone to use two sets of metaphors.   We can speak about heritage and inheritance, terms that refer to the transmission of property and material objects from the deceased to their heirs or social successors.   But we also use metaphors of genealogy, or the transmission of genetic substance from ancestors to descendants. "Genealogy" is a term that has gained a wider currency in the two decades through the influence of Foucault, who took it from Nietzsche but gave it a somewhat paradoxical spin.[2] For where we might regard its intrinsic thrust as being to underscore the continuity from past to present, Foucault uses it to highlight the *dis*continuities of history, to point up the radical otherness of our predecessors' conceptions and practices. From an evolutionary perspective this can be accommodated: the substance of evolution is, after all, "descent *with modifications*".

But there is another problem. In the cultural field, affinities across time don't just occur because of the influence of the past on the present, but through the selective power of the present on the past. The active years of my Spencer scholarship were an interlude in a career mainly devoted to African studies; and one thing that any sociologist of the Yoruba knows is that while the genealogies he collects are supposed to record the patrilineal transmission of a mystical identity, as occurs with the Y chromosome, what happens in practice is that genealogies are socially constructed and continually revised so that the contemporary realities of power are expressed in the normative form of patrilineal descent. So it is with intellectual genealogies: the ancestors or so-called "founding fathers" of sociology are not absolutely given to it, but are forever being promoted or demoted, edited and interpreted, by their descendants. It is not a one-way process of past-to-present influence, but something more like a dialogue. We come to it already partly formed by these ancestors – for example, when we talk of social structures and functions we already reveal how marked we are by the influence of Spencer – and the texts are there, but it is *as if* through a conversation with them that we both fashion ourselves and re-fashion our ancestry. Putting this another way, we might liken the works of past thinkers to a stock of inherited materials which have already profoundly shaped what we are, but whose present and future impact depends on a continuous process of cultural selection mediated through the structures of memory.[3]

2.

We must start from a recognition that Spencer's tremendous reputation in the last decades of the nineteenth century, across many fields and in many countries, has not on the whole been matched by the judgement of posterity: he has not worn well. Let us briefly remind ourselves of the singularity of the achievement.

Born into modest circumstances in a Midlands town, and a family milieu that blended evangelical Christianity, scientific interests and radical middle-class politics, Spencer seems in a way to have been made for his age.   With little formal education (though a good grounding in the basic science of the day), he was able to seize the opportunities presented by the 1840s, that remarkable decade in which Britain finally realised itself as the world's first industrial society.   Via railway engineering, some intermittent political activism, attempts to market some small inventions, and finally journalism, he got to London in 1848 – the same year as his close contemporary Karl Marx – and two years later made a literary mark with his first book, *Social Statics*, a grounding of his radical-liberal ethics in the argument that the human character to make it possible was gradually (and inevitably) being perfected through a process of adaptation to "the social state".   Its Lamarckian language pointed strongly towards the evolutionary synthesis that he would forge over the next decade and spend the rest of his long life working out.

An independent man who never held a formal position after he gave up being sub-editor of *The Economist*, Spencer was able to support himself first from some modest bequests and eventually from the proceeds of his writing.   Notably quirky and non-conformist, he yet built up an extensive network of friends and acquaintances that ramified into many different fields, from a more literary circle round George Eliot and her partner G.H. Lewes, to T.H. Huxley and the scientists, a select group of whom joined Spencer in the famous X Club.   It was in the late 1860s that his reputation began to soar, as the successive volumes of *The System of Synthetic Philosophy* – from epistemology and metaphysics through biology, psychology and sociology to ethics – started to appear. The publication of *The Origin of Species* in 1859 had put organic evolution right at the centre of serious intellectual concern, and Spencer (who embraced it himself nearly a decade before and did more than anyone else to put the *word* "evolution" into currency) was looked to as providing the most systematic grounding and application of the evolutionary principle in every sphere of life and thought.

When Spencer died in 1903, the prevailing obituary judgement was that – though many of his key ideas were becoming *passe* – he had still been one of the intellectual giants of the Victorian age: phrases like "the last heroic figure of an age without equal" and "the last great man of the nineteenth century" were freely used.[4] And few of his contemporaries had as great an international impact. He had been translated into all the major European languages by the 1880s, and can crop up almost anywhere as a key reference point: Nietzsche's critical remarks about Spencer and the "English psychologists" in the *Genealogy of Morals* are typical.[5] On his vast influence in America in the last quarter of the nineteenth century, more shortly. Most remarkable of all was the way he was taken up beyond Europe and America – in Japan, China, India and the Middle East – where he stood for something rather momentous: a vision of the path to modernity that attracted intellectuals of the East because it did not entail passing through the portals of Christianity.

Such is the singularity, range, and influence of Spencer's work, and the centrality of his contribution to the intellectual culture of the Victorian age, that it is more than surprising that he, uniquely for a figure of his importance, has attracted no full-scale modern biography, or systematic study of his life and thought. Yet literary biography is a highly flourishing genre, with novelists, artists and poets as the most attractive subjects – not surprisingly, since their lives seem to have been more rackety than those of philosophers and scientists. Probably as few people read Carlyle now as read Spencer, but anyone can see that the storms and sulks of the Carlyles' marriage have a human interest that the pooterishness of *Home Life with Herbert Spencer*[6] cannot rise to; and the lack of much sex-interest in Spencer's life is hardly compensated by an account of his personal eccentricities. George Eliot was all too right when she said that "the life of this philosopher, like that of the great Kant, offers little material for the narrator".

Compared with other major thinkers of the nineteenth century, Spencer would not now be considered a figure of equal importance to Darwin, Marx and Freud, whose lives and works have attracted innumerable studies. We remember each of these for a single, original analytical insight – natural selection, class struggle, the unconscious – whose thrust was to make a major sphere of human existence look radically different, reshaping for ever how Europeans viewed themselves: their place in nature, their social relations, their sense of self. By contrast, Spencer's achievement was not revolutionary in the same way. It was (to use a favourite word of his) synthetic: it involved drawing together the best current thinking in various spheres, reconciling their contradictions and discerning common principles beneath diverse phenomena, creating the vision of an enlarged zone of order in which new moral and intellectual agendas could be pursued.

While Spencer is usually paired off against either Darwin or Marx, with J.S. Mill and Auguste Comte he forms part of a triangle of mixed affinities and contrasts. They too were synthetic thinkers. Mill, who sought to soften utilitarianism's hard edges and reconcile it with the humane values of the age, was in many ways less original and far-reaching than Spencer. If he is almost canonised as a saint of Liberalism (and now of feminism too), that is due less to his magisterial syntheses on logic and political economy than to the classic qualities of his essay *On Liberty*, and his poignant *Autobiography*. Spencer's *Autobiography* is a fascinating document too – it was what turned me on to Spencer – but it does not convey a man of the human stature of Mill; and that too affects how we remember them.   Overall, Comte's *oeuvre* comes closest to Spencer's, as a philosophy of science linked to a political vision – albeit a very different one – but Spencer's synthesis was more cogent and was less purely legislative: he delivered much more at the concrete level of biology, psychology and sociology.   But the main point I want to make in comparing Comte and Spencer, is to do with how they are remembered.   To judge by what his biographer Mary Pickering says[7], Comte is as little, if not less, read than Spencer, yet in France he is prominently memorialised: a statue in the Place de la Sorbonne, and a street named after him in the *Sixieme Arrondissement*. For the French are very serious about creating *lieux de memoire*; and positivism, for all its eccentricities, became a tradition of the Third Republic.[8]   Spencer's Dissenting outsiderness, which is quite essential to his outlook, is underscored in the fact that there isn't even a blue plaque on either of the two houses where he lived for years in London.[9] It serves to remind us that the institutional conditions of social remembrance are as important as the intellectual ones.

3.

The publication in 1993 of Robert Perrin's invaluable *Bibliography,* with its 3082 items by and about Spencer, enables us to construct a rough statistical profile of the vagaries of his reputation since his death.[10] Aggregating these by decade, we find that over a quarter of all the posthumous references to him occur in the first ten years, 1903-12. Thereafter they drop sharply to a low point in the 1940s, but then gradually pick up, peaking again in the 1970s but slipping again somewhat in the 1980s. When we compare citations across disciplines, some interesting variations emerge. Interest in the philosophical aspects of Spencer's work was fairly high up to the First World War, but fell off sharply for several decades before picking up somewhat in the 1960s and 1970s; but while his sociology evoked a lower interest at the beginning of the century, it absolutely dominated the revival of the 1960s-70s. Politics shows a pattern of its own: a lower level overall than philosophy or sociology, but with modest peaks in 1913-22 and 1933-42, decades of militarism where people started to wonder if the pacific Spencer did not have something to teach them after all. The late 1980s and 1990s brought a particular resurgence of interest in his political philosophy, linked to the resurgence of anti-statist policies in the Thatcher/Reagan years. Citations in biology and psychology run generally at lower levels throughout, with relatively more interest in Spencer's biology up to the 1930s, and more in his psychology in the 1960s and 1970s.

So the temporal patterning of the collective memory of Spencer is pretty clear: a sharp decline not long after his death, a trough of several decades, and a modest revival, especially among sociologists, since the 1960s. But the trajectory shows significant differences between Britain and America. In Britain, despite the celebrity of his later years, Spencer was always an outsider, albeit a self-willed one: he was contemptuous of most established education, and declined all offers of academic posts and honours, including an invitation to become a founding member of the British Academy (for "metaphysics") in 1902. Darwin never held an academic post either, but still he was institutionally well connected; and in T.H. Huxley he had a redoubtable advocate who was a pivot of the public world of science and ensured that Darwinian theory was built into the agendas of the new university biology departments. But Spencer could hardly exploit his close links with Beatrice Webb in the same way, since her project for the LSE to link sociology and public policy was anathema to him. The "curious collection of eugenicists, urban planners, charity organizers, social statisticians and all-purpose do-gooders", as the founders of the British Sociological Association in 1903 have been described,[11] were not at all Spencer's kind of people. Yet still an ideal of social evolution derivative of Spencer's, mediated through L.T. Hobhouse, long continued to frame LSE sociology[12] – although it had ominously few implications for current research practice. When the Herbert Spencer Trustees decided to wind up their posthumous publication programme of Spencer's *Descriptive Sociology* series, their last act was to commission Jay Rumney's *Herbert Spencer's Sociology* (1934) with a Preface written by Morris Ginsberg, Hobhouse's successor at LSE. For all its pious conclusion that sociology would do well to build on Spencerian foundations, the tone of Rumney's work was valedictory; and in fact it ushered in the thirty-year trough in his reputation.

In America things were different. Here Spencer did have a kind of Huxley, in the person of Edward L. Youmans, who from the late 1860s promoted his work and in 1872 founded the long-lived *Popular Science Monthly*, which was a major vehicle for its diffusion. Spencer's outsiderness did not count against him in America, partly since its own academic institutions were still so flexible and unformed. Sure, there was a great furore at Yale when W.G. Sumner adopted *The Study of Sociology* – written at the instance of Youmans – as a course text in the late 1870s. But a few decades later the intellectual historian Vernon Parrington looked back to judge that Spencer had "laid out the broad pathway over which American thought travelled in the later years of the [19th]

Century".[13] He rightly meant much more by this than the vulgar reduction of Spencer's influence to the articulation of a dominant ideology of social-Darwinist *laissez-faire,* for what often captured the imagination of Americans was Spencer's unification of the sciences, or his vision of evolution as a vast cosmic process. This was what drew socialist or progressive novelists such as Jack London or – to name a figure less often connected with Spencer – Theodore Dreiser, whose splendid *Trilogy of Desire* had an unlikely dual inspiration in the novels of Balzac and Spencer's *First Principles*.[14] And even if Americans disagreed with Spencer, as increasingly they did, he was the thinker they had to argue against. Lester Ward, who in 1906 became first President of the American Sociological Society (and developed a rather different conception of social evolution), reported a meeting of the Washington Society for Philosophical Inquiry in 1894 at which there was an "almost uninterrupted onslaught upon [Spencer's] doctrines"; but yet concluded that Spencer had "forced his way into every department of human thought and action ... until today the eyes of the whole thinking world are centered upon him."[15]

Chicago, the setting for Dreiser's trilogy, is an excellent vantage-point from which to view the eventual downturn in Spencer's reputation even in America: for it was the crucible, not only of the melting-pot, urban-industrial society of the twentieth century, but of its most original social science. To get a picture of just how omnipresent and how diversely understood Spencer was in early twentieth century America, it's more helpful to turn away from academic writings to a work like Jane Addams's vivid memoir, *Twenty Years at Hull-House* (1910). Addams later won the Nobel Peace Prize, but her primary achievement was to found Hull-House, a settlement in Chicago's slums, inspired by the Christian Socialist model of Toynbee Hall in Whitechapel. Casual references to Spencer come twice into her narrative. A group of educated young men – many did voluntary work at Hull-House or joined in cultural activities there – jibbed at her "scathing remark that Herbert Spencer was not the only man who had ventured a solution to the riddles of the universe"; and the editor of an anarchist newspaper, during Kropotkin's visit to Chicago, "challenged the social order by the philosophic touchstone of Bakunin and of Herbert Spencer ..."[16]   Here we have Spencer invoked equally in support of conservative and of radical libertarianism.

The most original of the early Chicago sociologists was W.I. Thomas, who had been inspired to become a sociologist through reading Spencer, rather as Malinowski was converted to anthropology by reading Frazer.[17]   The Chicago School of Sociology flourished greatly over the next thirty years, and in 1929 moved into fine new quarters, the Social Science Research Building. Much trouble was taken with the design and décor of this building, and in the spandrels of the arches of its north portico were carved medallion portraits of six chosen pioneers of social science: Gibbon and Adam Smith, Bentham and Comte, Galton and Boas. A pair from each of the 18th, 19th and early 20th centuries, they seem chosen to express key antinomies: history vs. theory; individualism vs. collectivism (or utilitarianism vs. positivism), heredity vs. environment. No Spencer! The staple triad of today's sociological theory courses – Marx, Weber and Durkheim – are also absent. We seem to stand at a cusp in the development of the subject, as it turns its back on its recent, social evolutionary, past without certainty as to what lay before it. Weber was only just starting to be translated, and would not command serious attention till the 1930s, while Durkheim would arrive in Chicago in the luggage of Radcliffe-Brown in 1931.[18]   In cultural genealogies, unlike biological ones, it is usually the most recent ancestors who are the least secure: I doubt if Galton and Boas would be chosen for such commemoration today. But it makes good historical sense for them to be there then: because, in opposed but complementary ways, they enabled that generation to put Spencerian evolution decisively behind it – Galton because he stood for the acceptable Darwinian residue of natural selection working on a genetic inheritance, Boas because he saw the aim of anthropology as being to show how particular cultures developed in response to diverse local circumstances, not to discover a universal path of cultural evolution.

Spencer's fall from American grace occurred after the First World War. In 1916 there had been a re-issue of *The Man vs. The State*, with respectful comments by several eminent public figures, including Senators Henry Cabot Lodge and William H. Taft.[19] But by 1933 the political scientist Crane Brinton posed his famous rhetorical question – "Who now reads Herbert Spencer?" – that was taken up by Talcott Parsons in 1937, in the book that placed Weber and Durkheim in the sociological canon.[20] Spencer's eclipse occurred at two levels: his philosophical and social vision no longer meshed with the spirit of the times, as America reached its industrial maturity; and his theories lost their appeal in the academy as it became clear that they did not generate relevant research problems. The nadir of Spencer's reputation was evidenced in very different ways in two books, both published in 1944. The first is a classic in the field of Spencer studies, viz. Richard Hofstadter's *Social Darwinism in American Thought*.[21] Hofstadter shared the ideals of the New Deal era, and he did not aim to praise Spencer but to bury him, to register decisively that his time was past. The other was Friedrich von Hayek's polemic against collectivist thought, *The Road to Serfdom*. What is so striking here is that Hayek – then at LSE, later to go to Chicago – did not even mention Spencer, even though he had warned more forcefully of the threat to freedom posed by the modern state – "the coming slavery" was how he put it – than any other recent thinker. But Hayek wrote in a very different context, a world where a faith in national economic planning was widely shared across the entire political spectrum of wartime Britain. Granted his ideological affinity, Hayek's tacit erasure of Spencer ultimately says more than Hofstadter's historicism about just how much Spencer was now seen as an anachronism.

4.

Before the downturn in his reputation, Spencer was always read in a presentist mode – as someone whose ideas had an intrinsic interest, as possibly offering answers to the reader's questions – which is how Rumney still read him. But as he faded into the past, it became necessary for him to be read in a historicist mode, that is as an author whose work might shed light on how and why the predicament of the present differs from the past from which it has emerged. This was how Hofstadter read him. Yet even then, down to our own times, presentist readings are still made, even though they must make some allowance for the claims of the historicist approach. In the rest of the lecture, I shall focus on this mix of presentism and historicism in how Spencer has been taken up again since the 1960s. This has come from three main directions: from sociologists, from political theorists, and from those concerned with evolutionary theory in general, particularly in the light of the ambition to develop a new Darwinian synthesis of the human sciences.

Renewed interest in Spencer's sociology would hardly have happened without the boom in the subject itself, both in America and Britain, from the late 1950s onwards. Yet the first major reassessment – John Burrow's *Evolution and Society* (1966) – was an urbane study in intellectual history, which set Spencer, alongside Tylor and Maine, in a tradition of social thought running back to the eighteenth century. Burrow considered his own approach to the history of "Victorian social theory" quite different from what a social scientist might want to write, which would be largely a matter of evaluating past thinkers in terms of how far they anticipated modern ideas. A fresh reappraisal of the evolutionary tradition, he argued, was required by the fact that it had been so clearly repudiated by modern sociology and anthropology.[22] But that had never been as wholly the case as Burrow supposed, particularly in America; and in fact a revival of evolutionism more generally was already under way. Even in British anthropology, whose folk history still tends to hold that evolution was entirely displaced by the new paradigm of structural-functionalism, the evolutionary project, while little relevant to the field studies that now defined social anthropology, still lurked in the background. Radcliffe-Brown, the leading structural-functionalist, actually published lectures (in 1947 and 1958) in which he invoked Spencer on two points: firstly, that its objective should be to describe the evolution of *societies*, rather than cultures; and secondly that it should be seen as a process of differentiation in the forms of social life.[23]

There were soon reissues of Spencer's works. None other than Talcott Parsons wrote a forward to *The Study of Sociology* in 1961, professing to have rediscovered its value after 25 years of what he called "purposed neglect".[24] With an almost disarming vanity, what Parsons usually found of most value in prior thinkers was anticipations of his own latest thoughts. Now he praised Spencer for originating three ideas of enduring value: of society as a self-regulating system, of functional differentiation and of the idea of evolution. For Parsons was about to "come out" as an evolutionist himself, for reasons not derived from reading Spencer. *The Principles of Sociology* was too long for reissue in its entirety; but two decent volumes of selections came out in 1969 and in 1974, introduced respectively by Stanislav Andreski and by Robert Carneiro. Both had a long-standing interest in Spencerian themes. Under the guidance of Radcliffe-Brown, Andreski had written a pioneering study, *Military Organization and Society* (1954), considerably indebted to Spencer's concept of the "militant" society. As a refugee from communist Poland, Andreski had a visceral sympathy with Spencer's critique of the overweening state and regarded with contempt the appeal that various kinds of Marxism then had for Western sociologists. Yet Andreski was less interested in Spencer's theory of social evolution as an alternative to Marxism, than in what *The Principles* still had to offer to comparative sociology. Carneiro, by contrast, came from American cultural anthropology with an interest in the evolution of early states. It remains true that for straight presentist appreciation of Spencer, whether for his sociological analysis[25] or his libertarian politics, you have to go to America.

Yet it was also quite possible for a concern with the relevance of Spencer for current sociology to be combined with a historicist approach to his work. Here I would instance my own study of Spencer, which had as one motive to recover and celebrate the achievement of easily the most significant British founder of sociology.[26] In this there was an element of what might be called historical auto-anthropology, for I was intrigued by how the Midlands provincial culture of my own background had shaped Spencer's thought. A larger relevance came from the attempt by

Parsons and some of his disciples to revive a theory of social evolution. Of the viability of this neo-evolutionism I was sceptical, so my historicist treatment of Spencer's theory, in showing its intelligibility and cogency in relation to its own time, implied that it was not a model for ours. So while all treatments of past theorists are *interested*, in the sense of employing or validating particular methods or approaches, mine was doubly so, since it took a view – as Burrow's study did not – on what contemporary sociology should be. It was initially from the perspective of a sociologist working on the relations between religious and social development in contemporary Africa that I felt that neo-evolutionism was a less fruitful framework than a more open-ended historical sociology of the kind pioneered by Max Weber.

Parsons's turn to evolution may be seen as his most appropriate response to the charge repeatedly made against his functionalist theory of social systems; that it "could not explain social change". This charge was most forcefully made by those who felt that such a theory already existed in the form of Marxism. Classical Marxism can be regarded as "social evolutionary" in a very general sense, since it too portrayed the plot of history as a progression towards more complex social forms, achieved through humanity's struggle to master the external conditions of its existence. The young Spencer's notion of "the social state" even has some resemblance to Marx's utopia of the classless (and stateless) society. The main difference between the Marxist and the "bourgeois" versions of evolution lies less in what they supposed change led to, than in how it came about. With Marxism it proceeds dialectically from contradictions within the mode of production, while for Spencer and Parsons it arises from the functional differentiation of the social system, an adaptive response to environmental pressure, accompanied by higher levels of integration.

While Parsons was prepared to acknowledge some indebtedness to Spencer, he also claimed that his own neo-evolution had benefited from recent advances in biology that had shown the "fundamental continuity between general organic and socio-cultural evolution".[27] It is odd that he should have charged "earlier evolutionists" of treating these as "radically discontinuous", since the only one he names – Spencer – had categorically insisted that evolution was singular and universal: he set out its general basis in *First Principles*, and his Lamarckism enabled a plausible unity to be asserted between its operation in the organic and the super-organic spheres. But then, having used the cachet of neo-Darwinism to distance himself from Spencer, Parsons declares that "to be an evolutionist, one must define a general trend", which he sees as the "enhancement of adaptive capacity". But it is much more in the spirit of Spencer than of Darwin thus to focus on the course or direction of evolution. The distinctive feature of Darwin's theory of natural selection, by contrast, was that it focussed less on the direction of evolutionary change than on its mechanism, which was not predictive but compatible with any imaginable course of development.

The movement towards a modern evolutionary synthesis along neo-Darwinian lines has been gathering pace since the flurry of publications that marked the centenary of *The Origin of Species* in 1959. In one of those volumes, *A Century of Darwin*, edited by S.A. Barnett (and including contributions by such prominent biologists as Gavin de Beer and W.E. Le Gros Clark) the sole sociologist, D.G. MacRae, greatly downplayed the past, the present and probable future influence of Darwin on the social sciences.[28] This view of neo-Darwinian evolution remained dominant among social scientists, especially when E.O. Wilson's *Sociobiology* seemed to threaten a biological take-over.[29] But in recent years evolutionary psychology has begun to gain a significant response, especially from some anthropologists,[30] and as distinguished a sociologist as Gary Runciman has firmly declared his attachment to a framework of neo-Darwinian theory.

So how does Spencer stand within this context? Reviewing sociology's ancestry in his book *The Social Animal* (1998), Runciman adopts the conventional view that "we are all to some degree" Durkheimians, Marxists and Weberians now. But apparently not in the same measure Spencerians. For Runciman finds too much deeply flawed in him: his conception of evolution as "a cosmic process of mechanistic advance towards a harmonious equilibrium", his attempt to ground ethics in the laws of nature, and his supposed legitimation of "unfettered competition in pursuit of personal gain".[31]   Yet he passes over Spencer's conceptual innovations – of social structure and function, of institutions as the key to the comparative analysis of societies, of social differentiation as a core component in what anyone might want to call development – which he set to work in *The Principles of Sociology* and on which all later sociology rests. Spencer's dynamic functionalism deals in those relations between structures or practices and the conditions of particular environments, that Runciman wants neo-Darwinian sociology to address. So should we be surprised if in places *The Social Animal* evokes distinct echoes of Spencer's *Study of Sociology*? Runciman's contention that "the decisions of powerful people may be random inputs into the ongoing processes of cultural and social selection" puts one in mind of Spencer's robust treatment of the "great man theory of history"; and his criticism of "do-gooder sociology" for its facile assumption that the knowledge to solve social problems is easily found has a very Spencerian ring to it.[32]

So what accounts for this ambivalence towards Spencer? Runciman lightly identifies Spencerian social evolution with "Social Darwinism";[33] and associates that in turn with "fallacious racist nonsense", in contrast to "a genuinely 'Darwinian' sociology".[34] Spencer comes to be treated as the dark counterpart of Darwin, the unacceptable face of Darwinism, even a sort of scapegoat who can be used to carry away the sins of Darwinism. The pressure to do this arises from the tension we often sense between the iconic status we have accorded Darwin – not just a biologist of the highest importance but a loveable, even revered human being, the 4th or 5th Greatest Briton of all time, according to a BBC television poll – and the harsh or odious implications that have at one time or another been drawn from his theory. The irony is that the same tactic is also employed on the other side of the theoretical fence, as in the volume of essays, *Alas Poor Darwin: Arguments against Evolutionary Psychology*, edited by Steven and Hilary Rose. The very title gives it away: the authors aim to defend Darwin from what they seem to regard as the threat to his reputation posed by the appropriation of his ideas by the likes of Richard Dawkins, Daniel Dennett and Steven Pinker.

Now I don't want to enter into the scientific issues at stake here, except in so far as they touch on how Spencer is represented. Hilary Rose, a sociologist of science, has this to say about the relations of Darwin and Spencer:

> "What particularly drew Spencer [to evolutionary theory] was the importance Darwin gave to competition as the mechanism of natural selection. It was not Darwin but Spencer, followed by the poet Tennyson, who put into cultural circulation the savage metaphor of 'Nature red in tooth and claw'. Spencer (like today's EP theorists) was primarily interested in the mechanism of competition ... and relatively uninterested in Darwin's grand project of providing an account of transformation over time ... [Spencer's] was a fundamentally political project to explain why existing social hierarchies were natural and hence immutable".[35]

It cannot have been easy to pack so much error and confusion into just four sentences. Spencer was *not*, of course, drawn to evolutionary theory by Darwin. He was *not* the source of Tennyson's notorious metaphor of the cruelties of nature. (*In Memoriam* and *Social Statics* were published the same year, so chronology alone rules it out; and in any case the theory of natural selection was still eight years in the future). Spencer *was* essentially interested in accounting for change over time: what else could his ideas of adaptation to the social state, differentiation, and militancy-to-industrialism possibly be about? He did *not* think social hierarchies were immutable.

So though Runciman and Rose take diametrically opposed views of the merits of evolutionary psychology, they concur in projecting the objectionable features of Darwinism onto Spencer, via the notion of Social Darwinism. But Spencer is only plausible as Darwinism's fall-guy if his enduring Lamarckism is ignored or erased: we have to forget that almost the last major controversy in which Spencer engaged was his debate with August Weismann over the sufficiency of natural selection as a factor of evolution. Spencer insisted that the inheritance of acquired characteristics had an important role to play, particularly at the more advanced stages of evolution. The essential point at issue was more to do with how new traits are produced than with how they are later selected by (or adapted to) the needs of survival. The distinctive feature of Spencer's view, whether this is viewed as a flaw or a merit, is the space it gives to the organism's active engagement with its environment. This was what enabled Spencerian evolution to sit more easily with Victorian values of personal responsibility and moral improvement than the shocking originality of Darwinism's core idea: the process of natural selection working upon random genetic variations.

In these arguments, Social Darwinism often serves as a screen on which current concerns are played out. Anxiety about the ethical and political import of such Neo-Darwinist projects as sociobiology and evolutionary psychology was compounded by the electoral success of right-wing parties in both Britain and America during the 1980s, and by the intellectual and political disarray of the Left. When I first lectured on Spencer around 1970, his brand of anti-state individualism seemed almost archaic, but had its use as a theoretical counterpoint to the Marxism then in vogue. Then came Mrs Thatcher, who seems almost biographically predestined to have given him fresh relevance: lower-middle class origins in an East Midlands town, Methodism and self-help, an education biased towards natural science. A new British edition of *The Man versus The State*, the first for many years, a straw in the wind perhaps, had come out in 1969,[36] but there is no indication that she ever read Spencer: she got the doctrinal articulation of her anti-statism from Hayek. And of course there were components of Thatcherism that would have been obnoxious to Spencer, notably her aggressive patriotism. Indeed, one could hardly find a better way to show up the shallowness of much presentist interpretation of Spencer than to pose the hypothetical question: how could it once have made historical sense for someone to espouse domestic policies like Mrs Thatcher's and an attitude to foreign affairs more like Tony Benn's?

The revival of liberal individualism in practical politics – whether in the roll-back of the state from much of the economy, or in the new saliency of human rights discourse – has led in the 1990s to a significant rehabilitation of Spencer as a political theorist. The general terms of debate – freedom, justice, rights, order etc. – may be largely trans-historical, but the conditions under which any particular mix of them is plausible or realisable depends on the historical context. So we need to approach Spencer both as a theorist whose ideas need to be evaluated in their own terms, and as one who, belonging to a different context from ours, requires less to be engaged in argument than to be historically and culturally understood. What is good about the clutch of studies of Spencer's politics that have come out since 1992 is that, taken together, they provide these complementary perspectives. From one side, M.W. Taylor's *Men versus the State* (1992) impressively places Spencer's later political writings in that transitional period when the so-called "New Liberals" were seeking to temper classic Liberalism's suspicion of state intervention.[37] Spencer's libertarianism now made him a strong defender of private property, and so what we might call conservative, though he still opened *The Man versus the State* by asserting that "Most of those who now pass as Liberals are Tories of a new type".

Spencer liked to make an argument by taking an antinomy or pair of alternatives – utility vs. *laissez-faire*, freedom vs. justice, egoism vs. altruism, inductive vs. deductive reasoning, associationism vs. innate character – and seeking in some way to reconcile them. These distinctions were drawn into his system from diverse fields, so the coherence of the whole was always problematic, especially when it came to be applied in new contexts, where shifts in the empirical reference of its terms were likely. In a counterpoint to Taylor, Tim Gray's *The Political Philosophy of Herbert Spencer* (1996) adopts a conceptual, rather than a contextual, approach, and seeks to resolve one of the longest running criticisms of Spencer, that there is a contradiction between his political individualism and his organicist sociology.[38] He shows that the critics have typically conflated two separate distinctions – organism vs. mechanism and individualism vs. collectivism – so failing to recognise that originality and coherence of Spencer's individualist but organicist vision of society.

These and other recent treatments of Spencer's politics[39] shows that it is no longer true, as I wrote in 1971, that "there is no tradition of Spencer studies".[40]   But there are problems in developing it. One is the sheer range of fields to which Spencer contributed, which creates problems for an increasingly specialised scholarship – an irony for the prophet of development as differentiation. Thus in literature there is Nancy Paxton's *George Eliot and Herbert Spencer: Feminism, Evolutionism and the Reconstruction of Gender* (1991), which at last gives worthy attention to a theme which has long bubbled away on the fringes of Spencer studies, through a close analysis of the interplay between her novels and his successive works, within the context of their 30-years friendship.[41] Another literary scholar, Christopher Herbert, in *Culture and Anomie* (1991), a study of the concept of culture as it emerged across diverse forms of writing in the late nineteenth century, gives an absolutely pivotal role to Spencer's analysis of the moral restraints of savage society in Volume I of *The Principles of Sociology*.[42]

But Spencer's contributions to the natural sciences are still severely neglected. This is especially true of his biology, save in relation to Darwinism. But a recent article by James Elwick on Spencer's attraction to the idea that certain invertebrates originated as compound organisms sheds fascinating light not just on zoological thinking in the years before Darwinian evolution took hold, but on the implicit parallels between biological and social organisation.[43] We are reminded again how much Spencer calls for cross-disciplinary treatment, and how demanding this is. More surprising and also more serious is the thinness of the follow-up to Robert M. Young's pioneering study of Spencer's psychology in his *Mind, Brain and Adaptation in the Nineteenth Century* (1970). *The Principles of Psychology* was pivotal in the development of Spencer's project as a whole: it was the bridge that connected his philosophical to his scientific concerns; and its first edition preceded the formulation of the *System of Synthetic Philosophy*, while its greatly enlarged second edition was its central component. It seems to have gone unnoticed in the present surge of evolutionary psychology that if anyone is to be honoured as the thinker who not only first imagined such a field but also proposed in some detail what it might look like, it is Spencer. Of course he will not provide us with direct answers to our current questions, but an understanding of how he sought to work out the interplay of past and present, of organised character and environmental challenge – issues still very much unresolved in current debates among evolutionary psychologists and their critics – can still be both suggestive and provocative.[44]

Spencer studies have shown a fresh *elan* in the last ten years, but the definitive intellectual biography we so badly need still seems to be some way in the future. Without it, a large gap must remain in our knowledge, alike of the complex evolution of Spencer's thought, of its role in the making of the Victorian world, and of the tangled history of all the sciences of man. In all this, our interpretation of him must now be predominantly in the historicist mode. Yet Spencer can still speak directly to us, in that persistent, cantankerous, indignant, non-conformist voice he has, ever concerned to balance his cardinal values of freedom and justice, within a realistic view of the natural conditions of human action. The revival of interest in Spencer's political (and by implication, ethical) thought was evidently stimulated by the rise of anti-statist economic policies in the West in the 1980s. But the state's retreat from the economic sphere has been increasingly complemented by its swelling ambition to engineer the social sphere through energetic legislation and the adoption of a highly directive "audit culture". Spencer's writings have a fresh potential relevance here, not because they accord with the spirit of our times, but because they challenge it. From a perspective within the British academic system, the disastrous effects of government target-setting, of market-rigging through partial state monopsony, of the imposition of ever more detailed regulation, of the whole culture of hyper-audit by agencies of the state, must make us hope that *The Man versus the State* never goes out of print.

Notes and References

1 D. N. Y. Peel, "The determinacy gene and environmental adaptation in the White Lupin (*Lupinus albus*)", Ph.D. thesis, University of Cambridge, 1997.

2 See his "Nietzsche, Genealogy, History" (1971), in D. Bouchard (ed.), *Language, Counter-Memory, Practice: Selected Essays and Interviews* (Ithaca, 1977), 139-164.

3 For an interesting application of the notion of "cultural selection", no doubt indebted to current neo-Darwinism but free of tendentious analogies such as the concept "meme", see Gary Taylor, *Cultural Selection: Why Some Achievements Survive the Test of Time-And Others Don't* (New York 1996).

4 Obituaries in *The Independent* 55 (1903); *The Illustrated London News*, 12 December 1903.

5 F. Nietzsche, *On the Genealogy of Morals*, translated by Douglas Smith (Oxford, 1996 [1887]), 14, 59.

6 Two, *Home Life with Herbert Spencer* (Bristol, 1906). These were the ladies – Perrin says there were actually three of them – who kept house for him during 1889-98. Cf. G. and W. Grossmith, *The Diary of a Nobody* (London, 1892), though Holloway was more down-market than St John's Wood.

7 Mary Pickering, *Auguste Comte: An Intellectual Biography* (Cambridge, 1993), vol. 1, 1.

8 See the great work of Pierre Nora and his associates, *Realms of Memory: The Construction of the French Past*, English language edn. prepared by Lawrence D. Kritzman, 3 vols. (New York).

9 38, Queens Gardens, Bayswater and 64, Avenue Road, St Johns Wood. The former, a stuccoed terrace, is much as it would have been; the latter has evidently been replaced by a mansion of 1930s Georgian appearance. His last residence in Brighton, I am told, has a plaque. The house where he was born in Derby was demolished c.1969, but there is a bronze medallion to him (and other local worthies, including Erasmus Darwin) on the Derwent Bridge in Derby.

10 Robert G. Perrin, *Herbert Spencer: A Primary and Secondary Bibliography* (New York, 1993).

11 Philip Abrams, *The Origins of British Sociology 1834-1914* (Chicago, 1986),

12 On whom see Stefan Collini, *Liberalism and Sociology* (Cambridge, 1979).

[13] Vernon L. Parrington, *Main Currents in American Thought*, vol. 3 (New York, 1930),

[14] Richard Lingeman, "Introduction", New American Library edition of Theodore Dreiser, *The Stoic* (New York, 1981), vii.

[15] Lester Ward, "Spencer-smashing at Washington", *Popular Science Monthly* 44 (1894), 856-858, cited by Perrin, *Herbert Spencer*, 654.

[16] Jane Addams, *Twenty Years at Hull-House*, New American Library edition (New York, 1981), 242, 279.

[17] Martin Bulmer, *The Chicago School of Sociology* (Chicago, 1984), 36.

[18] Talcott Parsons's translation of *The Protestant Ethic and the Spirit of Capitalism* appeared in 1930; George Simpson's of Durkheim's *The Division of Labour in Society* in 1933.

[19] Truxton Beale (ed), *The Man versus the State: A Collection of Essays by Herbert Spencer* (New York, 1916).

[20] Talcott Parsons, *The Structure of Social Action* (New York, 1937).

[21] First edition, Philadelphia, 1944; second edition, Boston 1955.

[22] J.W. Burrow, *Evolution and Society: A Study in Victorian Social Theory* (Cambridge, 1966), ix.

[23] A. R. Radcliffe-Brown, "Evolution: social or cultural", *American Anthropologist* 49 (1947), 78-83; "Social evolution", in *Method in Social Anthropology* (London, 1958), 178-189.

[24] T. Parsons, Introduction to reprint of H. Spencer, *The Study of Sociology* (New York, 1961).

[25] E.g. Jonathan H. Turner, *Herbert Spencer: A Renewed Appreciation* (Beverly Hills, 1985); or his article on Spencer in *The International Encyclopedia of the Social and Behavioral Sciences* (Amsterdam and New York, 2001), 22: 14894-98, especially its concluding section regretting the neglect of Spencer, entitled "What might have been and can still be".

[26] J.D.Y. Peel, *Herbert Spencer: The Evolution of A Sociologist* (London, 1971).

[27] T. Parsons, *Societies: Comparative and Evolutionary Perspectives* (Englewood Cliffs, 1966), 109-110.

[28] D.G. MacRae, "Darwinism and the social sciences", in S.A. Barnett (ed.), *A Century of Darwin* (London, 1988). 296-312.

[29] See, for example, Marshall Sahlins, *The Use and Abuse of Biology: An Anthropological Critique of Sociobiology* (Ann Arbor, 1976).

30 E.g., Pascal Boyer, *Religion Explained: The Human Instincts that Fashion Gods, Spirits and Ancestors* (London, 2001); Harvey Whitehouse, *Arguments and Icons: Divergent Modes of Religiosity* (Oxford, 2000).

31 W.G. Runciman, *The Social Animal* (London, 1998), 51-52. As for the third charge, anyone who thinks this of Spencer should read his essays "Railway morals and railway policy" (*Edinburgh Review*, October 1854) and "The morals of trade" (*Westminster Review,* April 1859), both reprinted in *Essays: Scientific, Political, and Speculative,* vol. 2 (London, 1883).

32 *Ibid.* 154, 208-209.

33 In one of the most judicious recent discussions of the slippery concept of Social Darwinism, John Burrow reminds us that it is "a term of art, used by historians, rather than by its proponents", and suggests that it would best be "reserved for ideas which in a social context seem to try to mirror the concept which is Darwin's most specific contribution to the theory of evolution, namely natural selection": and that in particular it would clarify matters if "Social Darwinism" were distinguished from "Social Evolution": *The Crisis of Reason: European Thought, 1848-1914* (New Haven, 2000), 92-96.

34 *Ibid.,* 6, 140, 191-192.

35 Hilary Rose, "Colonizing the social sciences?", in Hilary and Steven Rose (eds.), *Alas Poor Darwin: Arguments against Evolutionary Psychology* (London, 2000).

36 D.G. MacRae (ed.), Herbert Spencer, *The Man Versus The State* (Harmondsworth, 1969). MacRae's 50-page Introduction is one of the best essays of its kind.

37 M.W. Taylor, *Men Versus the State: Herbert Spencer and Late Victorian Individualism* (Oxford, 1992).

38 T.S. Gray, *The Political Philosophy of Herbert Spencer: Individualism and Organicism* (Aldershot, 1996). See too his "Herbert Spencer: individualist or organicist", *Political Studies* 33 (1985), 236-253.

39 E.g. John Offer's edition of Spencer's *Political Writings* in the Cambridge Texts series (1994), the handsome treatment accorded Spencer in J.S. McClelland's comprehensive *History of Western Political Thought* (London, 1996), Chap. 21, or D. Weinstein's *Equal Freedom and Utility* (Cambridge, 1998) on Spencer as a Liberal Utilitarian.

40 Peel, *Herbert Spencer,* 6.

[41] Nancy L. Paxton, *George Eliot and Herbert Spencer: Feminism, Evolutionism and the Reconstruction of Gender* (Princeton, 1991).

[42] Christopher Herbert, *Culture and Anomie: The Ethnographic Imagination in the Nineteenth Century* (Chicago, 1991).

[43] J. Elwick, "Herbert Spencer and the disunity of the social organism", *History of Science* 41 (2003), 35-72. See too Greta Jones's valuable earlier study, *Social Darwinism and English Thought: The Interaction between Biological and Social Theory* (Brighton, 1980).

[44] Here one of the most penetrating discussions of Spencer has come from the anthropologist Tim Ingold. See his *Evolution and Social Life* (Cambridge, 1986).

Index

EUGENICS IN AUSTRALIA:

Striving for National Fitness

By

Diana Wyndham

CONTENTS

ISBN 0950406678

Available post paid from the Institute's General Secretary Price
£5.00

MARIE STOPES, EUGENICS AND THE ENGLISH BIRTH CONTROL MOVEMENT

EDITED BY ROBERT PEEL

Proceedings of the 1996 Conference of the Galton Institute

CONTENTS

ISBN 0950406627

Available post paid from the Institute's General Secretary Price
£5.00

ESSAYS IN THE HISTORY OF EUGENICS

EDITED BY ROBERT PEEL

Proceedings of the 1997 Conference of the Galton Institute

CONTENTS

ISBN 0950406635

Available post paid from the Institute's General Secretary Price
£5.00

HUMAN PEDIGREE STUDIES

EDITED BY ROBERT PEEL

Proceedings of the 1998 Conference of the Galton Institute

CONTENTS

ISBN 0950406643

Available post paid from the Institute's General Secretary Price
£5.00

POPULATION CRISES AND POPULATION CYCLES

BY

CLAIRE RUSSELL AND W M S RUSSELL

CONTENTS

ISBN 0950406651

Available post paid from the Institute's General Secretary Price £5.00

ALSO AVAILABLE

A CENTURY OF MENDELISM

EDITED BY ROBERT PEEL and JOHN TIMSON

Proceedings of the 2000 Conference of the Galton Institute

CONTENTS

Notes on the Contributors

ISBN 095040666X

Available post paid from the Institute's General Secretary Price
£5.00